BY WILLIAM INGE

My Son Is a
Splendid Driver

My Son Is a Splendid Driver

a novel by
WILLIAM INGE

An Atlantic Monthly Press Book
Little, Brown and Company — Boston – Toronto

LIBRARY OF CONGRESS CATALOG CARD NO. 79-147771

FIRST EDITION

T06/71

ATLANTIC—LITTLE, BROWN BOOKS
ARE PUBLISHED BY
LITTLE, BROWN AND COMPANY
IN ASSOCIATION WITH
THE ATLANTIC MONTHLY PRESS

Published simultaneously in Canada
by Little, Brown & Company (Canada) Limited

PRINTED IN THE UNITED STATES OF AMERICA

In memory of my mother,
Maude Sarah Gibson Inge

". . . woe to those who do not know their own misery and woe to those who love this wretched and corruptible life."

THOMAS À KEMPIS
The Imitation of Christ

Author's Note

I have written this novel in the form of a memoir, draw-ing freely upon life as I have known it. Much of it has been invented, the rest has been adapted to the needs of the story I wished to tell, and all of it is fiction.

I

Summer Ghosts

Prologue

Now that I have lived a half-century, it is hard to believe that I can remember gaslight, and the town lamplighter who rode by on his horse every evening to ignite the wicks in the lampposts, and then again every morning to douse them. He looked a mysterious figure out of some fable of Gothic romance, and his coming was always waited for like a herald's appearing to announce the night, telling us that dark was descending and it was time for us to go inside our houses and stay close within the comfort there. This period of time seems so far in the past, I wonder if it was really I who lived those few years before the use of electricity was commonplace. Now when I watch the television and see rockets fired to the moon and see the confident, leathery faces of the men who have guided them there, I feel my early childhood must have been another life, another incarnation, so little of it pertains to the present. And so it is with some compulsion that I write the story of the life and the lives that I knew, as they beg to be recorded. It's almost as if I heard some of these lives, now deceased, crying out of their graves for me to make some mention of the beauty, the vanity, the despair, the pride or the valor of their existence.

I.

M Y MOTHER was a high-strung little woman who never felt at peace except in her own home surrounded by her long-familiar neighbors. My father was seldom with us. He was a salesman who traveled for a wholesale drygoods house located in St. Louis, Missouri. Usually, he would be home for the weekend, but there were many times when he would have to be gone a month or more. In those days, a salesman like my father had an important job, breaking in new territory for his company, finding new customers for them in the dusty little towns of Kansas and Oklahoma that had one general store that sold groceries, household supplies, clothing, and hardware. A wholesale house was dependent upon men like my father to make friendly customers for them who would rely upon the company for supplies. It was a job that my father respected and worked at conscientiously. He was close to the president of the company and would sometimes spend weeks at a time in St. Louis with him, mapping out territories, planning campaigns like warlords plotting to take over rival territory. So at home we were accustomed to my father's absence, and to the nervous matriarchy that my mother brought us up in. She ran the house with the fretful uncertainty of a woman who never completely trusted her own authority but, lacking it from any other quarter, tried to persuade us children to abide by her decisions, even if she feared she was wrong.

It was a domestic kingdom my father had turned over to her freely, probably gladly; for men were restless in their homes at that time, just after the First World War, when law and order still were binding restrictions to Western men who, not many years before, had ridden the plains on horses, carrying loaded guns by their sides, ready to kill anything that appeared to threaten them. Men then were free to drink and gamble and whore, letting women live their own lives as they pleased, using them only as servants or to satisfy their own lusty pleasures. Probably my father had taken his job for the reason that he was restless and did not want to feel that his life was confined to the inside of a house, where a fretful wife and four willful children were nagging reminders of his lack of freedom. Mother often accused him of this, for he could have taken over his father's little department store in Garden City and become a respected merchant, and come home to his family every night as other husbands did, and been a daily help to my mother in raising us children. But my father had made his choice and didn't want to be reminded that he might have made a mistake, or acted out of weakness, or shirked a responsibility his father had left him. If Mother reminded him too often of the security he had spurned, he would turn the house blue with profanity, stalk out of the door, slamming it behind him, and drive downtown to the little office where he stored his trunks and sample cases, and drink from a bottle of bootleg whiskey he usually kept in his desk drawer. He was not ordinarily a drinking man, for he had seen his younger brother die of drink, and my father feared it; but it was an occasional solace to whatever regrets he suffered in his life, regrets he was always too proud to admit to us.

A trip, a journey, was always a fearful excitement for my mother to anticipate. In the summer of 1919, we decided to drive to Colorado Springs and have a vacation in the mountains, away from the searing heat of a Kansas summer. Mother had never traveled. She was born of young British parents who had come to this country a year before the Civil War, and her father had had to enlist, almost upon landing on our shores, to fight for the Union. After the war, he and my grandmother settled in a small town in Illinois where they began to raise their family. It was there my mother was born. My grandfather tried several ways of making a living, moving frequently to some new part of the country where fortune was reported more promising, before settling in Garden City, a little town in western Kansas, where he finally established himself as a dealer in harness ware. Until then, my mother's life had been nomadic. As the family moved from one town to another, she would be enrolled in a school only to have to leave after a few months and start in another. She got so far behind in her education she gave it up before finishing high school. It is a wonder to me that she was as literate as she was. She always spoke cultivated English. Undoubtedly she acquired her language habits as a child, listening to her parents, who were educated people. And she and her brothers had retained a slight British accent that always set them a little apart from their Midwestern neighbors.

The eldest girl in the family, Mother stayed home and helped to take care of the other children until she met and married my father and started a family of her own. So she had never traveled, she had only migrated when she was a child, in a way that was disturbing to her and must have left a permanent reflex on her emotions; for she behaved, each time we planned a trip, as though she were saying goodbye to all that was dear and familiar to her, and making a voyage into the terrors of the unknown. Weeks before we finally started for Colorado, in a big Buick touring car that my father had just bought for family use (he had his own car for his work), Mother began to suffer fears of possible catastrophes that could destroy us on the way. "Oh, I hear those high mountain roads are terribly dangerous," she whimpered to my brother Julian, who would do most of the driving. He was just out of high school and was the man of the family in my father's usual absence. He was a moody young man, considered by our neighbors to be "wild," for he was one of a gang of boys who liked to drive their cars at high speed through the streets of the town, and who were known to smoke cigarettes (which were sold against the law in Kansas at that time), and who were occasionally seen with some of the young women in town who had bad reputations for their boldness with men. But whatever Jule's behavior away from home, he was always angelic with Mother, tenderly considerate of her most childish and unreasonable fears, and with a talent for persuading her out of them.

"You're not going to be afraid with me at the wheel, are you, Mother? Don't you trust my driving? I'm not afraid of those old mountain roads."

Then Mother's fear would vanish like a shadow, and she would smile and say, "Of course not. You're a splendid driver. I'm not going to worry any more." And for a day or so, she would go about her housework with happy relief and even dare to look forward to the trip with joy, until some other fear would find its way to her expectant heart that trembled to receive it.

Our home now was in Freedom, a small, prosperous town in the southeastern part of Kansas where the geography was nothing like that of the flat, dry western half of the state where Mother and Father had met. They had moved here early in the century, when my sister Treva was just a few years old and Julian a baby. Soon another baby was born, a little girl who died in infancy, a tragedy Mother still brooded over. Later, my sister Grace was born, and five years after that, myself. My mother had never been back to Garden City in the fifteen or more years since they had moved. As a child, I could not imagine my parents had ever lived anywhere except in the pretty and prosperous town that was now our home, with its spacious houses and wide green lawns, all tented over by the heavy foliage of great elm trees and maples, where the surrounding country was verdant and hilly.

When my parents left western Kansas, Indians were still an occasional threat to travelers, and there were still marauding bandits and treacherous gypsies, left over from the lawless days of notorious Dodge City. The country my parents had left was barely civilized. Mother shuddered at the thought of returning. "We're not living in pioneer days, Mother," Jule argued with her. "Indians don't shoot arrows at you any more. They're all driving around in Packards and Cadillacs." (At this time, some Indians were very wealthy from the money the government had paid for the land that white men had previously taken from them.) Mother smiled for him, to show that she appreciated his attempt to humor her, but her fear remained. "I'm taking my gun along, Mother. I'll keep it on the floor in the front seat where I'll be able to grab it when we see any desperadoes. You won't have to worry."

Mother's fears did not cease until the day before we

left, when we began to pack. Then she was too busy to entertain her fears. She had to see that we all packed clothes enough to last us for the summer, and that we took her favorite cooking utensils, for she didn't know for sure what the house we had taken for rent, without even seeing, would provide. The day of our leaving, we were up early to help Father and Jule pack all of our suitcases and bundles into the trunk at the rear of the car, and onto the running board. "We look like a band of gypsies ourselves, don't we?" Mother laughed when she looked at the loaded Buick. And now, her preliminary fears already faced, she felt a happy excitement when Father locked the house up tight, leaving the keys with a neighbor, and we got into the car to leave. Mother sat in the front seat with Jule (his gun on the floor as he promised), Father, Grace and I in the back.

My sister Treva was not with us that morning. She was making the trip with her fiancé, Clinton Murray, a wealthy young man whose engagement ring she wore, and whom she intended to marry as soon as he graduated from the college he was attending in the East. He and Treva and his mother were driving together in his new Cadillac coupé. Treva had taken her luggage to the Murrays' house the day before and had dinner with Clinton and his family and spent the night with them in order to get an early start in the morning. We didn't expect to see her again until we got to Colorado Springs. She would be at the Broadmoor Hotel, she had informed us, as casually as if she had always been in a position to take luxury for granted. "We'll probably get there long before you all do."

Jule ruffled at the implication he was not as good a driver as Clinton Murray.

"Just call me at the Broadmoor when you arrive, and I'll join you," she said.

Clint had been taking her luggage out to his Cadillac. When he came back, they both said goodbye to us and went to his house where she and the family would be served dinner by a maid, and she would spend the night in a big, airy room in which all the linens were scented with lavender.

Treva had never seemed to belong wholly to our family. She was the firstborn, and the first grandchild to both sets of grandparents, who were so proud they claimed her as their own and pampered her with gifts from the day of her birth. My father made enough money to support us all comfortably, but Treva had been brought up (unlike the rest of us) favored like a princess. She had an eye and taste for quality in her belongings. Sometimes it was a strain on Father to buy her the expensive clothes that she expected as her right to own and wear, but as he was in the drygoods business, he was able to get them at wholesale prices. So she was able to dress with the expensive taste that seemed innate in her. And she was beautiful. To Grace and me, her life was a fairy tale of parties and romance. She was the imagined heroine of every story we read. But if Jule, a year and a half younger than Treva, sometimes resented the advantages she displayed over the rest of the family, he can hardly be blamed.

During the months when Clinton was away at school, Treva and Jule contested each other almost nightly for use of the family car, and Jule would have to accede to her over and over for the mere fact that she was a young lady, which didn't always impress him as it was expected to. "She thinks she's better than the rest of us, just because she's engaged to Clint Murray," he used to complain to Mother.

"Now, son," she would pacify him after Treva had driven off in the Buick to stop by for Peg and Sally to take them over to Irene's house where they would make fudge and play cards, or maybe go to a movie.

"She does. She thinks she's better than we are. But she's not. She's just got a lot of put-on airs. At heart, I bet she's no better than old Bonnie Sherman."

"Jule! You mustn't say that. That's not true. Your sister is a young lady. We mustn't even speak of her in the same breath with the name of a woman like Bonnie Sherman. Now you must take that back, Jule. Promise me you'll take that back and say you didn't mean it. Promise me."

Probably there was a woman like Bonnie Sherman in every small town in the Midwest, maybe in the East, too, and in the South. A woman who, in her youth, had become pregnant by a man who did not want to marry her and so had run off and left her to face society alone with her child. She was then in her mid-twenties, still with some prettiness of face and figure, even though she cheapened her appearance by peroxiding her hair and painting her face heavily with rouge and lipstick and mascara, all of which, at that time, were the advertisements of a prostitute.

Respectable women permitted themselves the use of face powder, but other cosmetics, until a few years later, were used sparingly if at all by women who expected social approval. But Bonnie, according to the women who had known her before her disgrace, the women who had been her friends through the days of high school and young people's church socials, had been "as nice and respectable as any girl in her class." Still, they could not forgive her her breach of their moral code. Bonnie had faced her situation with courage. When it became unmistakably evident that she was with child, she lost all of her friends in the day or two that it took for the story to spread over the town. Suddenly, she was a deserted woman, who appeared on the streets alone whenever she had to come to town to do some shopping. Her former friends spoke to her cautiously, so as not to risk involving themselves in her predicament, or to give her any encouragement that their friendship could be resumed. Yet she always faced them with a pleasant smile, a smile that understood their attitude, a smile that became a little twisted by irony after a few years, and that seemed to mock them a little, her friends, as if in her heart she knew it was not her own weakness that caused them to abandon her, but theirs. The baby was given away for adoption.

Inasmuch as Bonnie hadn't the money to leave the town and live elsewhere, or the training for any kind of a job in case anyone might hire her, she fell into the only life that was left for her in Freedom, that of a streetwalker. Every night, she could be seen making her way through the main street of the town, knowing that everyone who saw her knew that she was going to the railroad depot to meet the nine o'clock train from Kansas City, to make herself available for any strange man who might be getting off the train to spend a day or two in town on business and want her company for some part of his stay.

She lived with an older sister, a spinster who worked at the public library. They were never seen together. The sister was a regular Sunday attendant at the Methodist Church, and attended all public functions alone, or with one of the other librarians. It was difficult to imagine the two sisters having any kind of communication in the old house they lived in together, the house of their deceased parents. Some people said they never spoke to each other and ate their meals separately.

I would like to say that my own mother, and that Jule and Treva, and all the other people I loved during my childhood, had been able to treat Bonnie Sherman, or at least refer to her, with respect, but I cannot claim this virtue for them. This was long before the teachings of Freud had taken hold in the public mind, at least in the culture of small American towns, and long after the teachings of Christ had been misused or forgotten. Sex was as fearful as black magic to all of us. Even a married woman could not honorably claim that she had any desire for her husband, and the male was forced to look upon his own desires as something ignoble. In retrospect, we all seem thwarted people.

My brother's accusations against Treva were not without semblance of truth. Treva was by nature a flirt. She may not have been conscious of the smile that appeared on her face and of the brightness that lit her eyes whenever she found herself in the company of an attractive man; but these things always happened, and Jule was quick to perceive them, as were the men themselves who were immediately attracted to Treva.

During the months when Clint was away at school, even though she wore his engagement ring, Treva accepted dates with other men. This shocked Jule.

"How can she do a thing like that, Mother, when she's supposed to marry Clint?"

Mother never pretended to judge her behavior. Treva's young will was stronger than Mother's slowly fading power to govern her children. She only tried to pacify my brother. "I'm sure your sister is doing no wrong, Jule. She just wants a good time. That's natural, isn't it? She can't sit at home all winter long and never go out to dances or parties just because Clint is gone. Clint doesn't expect her to." Jule wouldn't argue with Mother, and he was too noble to labor his accusations; but he sometimes glowered with resentment.

By the time Treva was eighteen, Mother had completely acceded to her taste in matters of dress and decor. Mother never bought clothes for herself or Grace without consulting Treva; and she never bought a new piece of furniture for the house or hung a picture without Treva's approval.

Eventually, Treva redecorated the house the way she wanted it, and we all had to admit the improvement, all but Jule who, if he did notice, wasn't willing to give Treva credit. He never made any comment on what she had done.

"If he had *his* way," Treva got back at him through Mother, "he'd have us all living in a billiard parlor. That's how much *he* cares." And she was largely right. Jule's physical surroundings mattered little to him as long as he had a soft chair by the fire to sit in after dinner and read his favorite stories in the *Saturday Evening Post* or *Red Book*, and a table nearby with an ashtray on it and matches and pipe-cleaners.

Jule could react perversely at times to Treva's continuing campaign to bring style and distinction to our home.

The more she sought to improve appearances, the more he sought to destroy them by refusing to dress for dinner in anything but the flannel shirts and corduroy riding breeches and high-laced boots that he wore daily to school in case there was a chance to go hunting in the afternoon when school let out. He was a constant provocation to Treva.

"Jule!" she would rail at him, "can't you find any place to keep those smelly pipe-cleaners so they don't stink up the living room?" Or "Jule! Would you please be considerate enough to clean out the bathtub when you've finished using it?" Or "Jule! would you *please* clean those muddy boots of yours before you come into the house?"

On more personal matters, concerning both Jule and me, she felt she had to use Mother as a mediator. "Mother, would you please tell Jule and Joey that a gentleman is expected to put the seat back down after he's stood up to use the toilet?" Mother would tell us. And "Mother! It's too humiliating to have to *hear* them when they use the toilet standing up. Last night, when Peg and I were sitting downstairs looking at my picture album, we could *hear* Jule as clear as if he'd been in the same room."

"But, Treva, both Joey and Jule always shut the door when they're using the bathroom."

"But you can still hear them, unless there's a lot of noise downstairs. Can't you tell them to run the tap water while they're doing it?"

Jule was infuriated when he got word of this ultimatum. "Goddamn it, it's getting to the place where a man can't even take a leak in his own home without getting criticized by her majesty."

Mother always flinched at his bursts of profanity. "Now, Jule, she doesn't mean to criticize."

"Has she been elected president around here?" he demanded. "Does she have the final say about everything that goes on in this house? Does she? Tell me the truth, Mother, because if she does, I'm going to move out *now*. If this is Treva's house, I don't want any part of it. I'll find a job and a house of my own and piss on the living room carpet if I feel like it. And her majesty can stay here and play like she's the Queen of Sheba for all I care."

It shattered Mother to hear Jule even threaten to move. "Oh, Jule, you don't mean it. You wouldn't move away from us, Jule. Now please don't be angry. Treva doesn't mean to be critical. She's at an age when girls can be kind of finicky, and she *does* want things to be nice when she entertains guests. You can understand that, can't you, Jule? Please don't be cross. I know Treva can be a little unreasonable at times. I'll talk with her. Now everything's going to be all right. You just forget it, Jule. Just forget I said anything about it, at all."

Jule was not a man of wit, or sarcasm, or cunning. He never sought deliberate revenge on Treva, and except for occasional head-on battles between them, he kept a sullen silence in her presence, and she pretended he did not exist. But when their resentment of each other, upon some sudden, unexpected provocation, would bring them into an open clash, they became like young tigers, I thought, tearing at each other with jealous ferocity.

"Go on down to your smoky old pool hall, and hang around with your trampy friends if you don't like things the way they are here. Or maybe you'd like to invite Bonnie Sherman over and entertain *her* in our parlor. Is that the way you'd like the house to be run?" Treva had picked up a glass vase and thrown it at Jule, cutting the hand he used to protect his face from getting hit. Then he slapped her, so hard that she reeled and almost fell to the floor, and called her a name I had never heard before, but which I knew as if by instinct was the most damning thing a man could call a woman. "You ornery *bitch*! Bonnie Sherman's a lot better'n *you*. Cause you're what all the guys in town call a *tease*. Yah. That's what you are, a *tease*. You flirt with guys, just to make 'em fall for ya whether you like them or not. You're nothing but an ornery *tease*."

When Treva recovered from the shock of his blow, she found ready possession of herself, and glared at Jule with a calm that was all the more damning because she had the confidence to put anger aside. "I despise you," she said, as if delivering a final judgment, and drew majestically up the stairs to her room, shutting the door behind her, leaving us all in a silence that filled us with the awe of revelation.

It was rare that Jule ever found a chance to get even with Treva, or to humiliate her in the way he felt she sometimes humiliated him. One of these chances came to him when he returned one evening from hunting, having been warned in advance that Clinton was home from school and Treva was having a dinner party, and that Jule would have dinner in the kitchen with Mother and Grace and me.

Treva had hired the Negro woman in town who cooked for parties to cook and serve the dinner, and there were a dozen guests at the table, young men and women who were Treva's friends, dining by candlelight. Jule would probably have been thoughtful enough to enter by the back door if he had remembered the party, but he had not; so it was necessary for him to pass through the dining room, with several dead squirrels over his shoulder, on his way to the kitchen. But maybe he planned it thus. His appearance, however, did not annoy Treva, despite the bloody squirrels, for her friends all knew Jule and liked him, as most people in town did, and the dinner was not so formal as to make his passage through the dining room too unseemly. Jule spoke to the guests good-naturedly and they all complimented him on his game. If he had just passed on into the kitchen then, Treva would have had no grievance, and the dinner conversation would have picked up from where it had left off as they went on eating the baked ham and asparagus with hollandaise. But Jule suddenly noticed the candlelight.

"Hey! What's happened to the electricity? Someone forget to pay the bill?"

It was probably the high point of the evening's entertainment for Treva's guests. Jule passed into the kitchen with something like a smirk on his face, but Treva had to sit through her guests' laughter and contain her humiliation. The rest of the dinner was for her like ashes. If ever she had seriously wanted to kill Jule, this probably was the time.

She cried on Mother's shoulder after the guests had gone. "How *could* he have said such a thing? How could he have embarrassed me so before my guests? He's *uncouth*, Mother. He *is*. I don't believe he's my brother. He couldn't be. There's no one else in the family who's such a devil."

2.

IT WAS A SUNNY JUNE MORNING when we started for Colorado. We all sat in the car waiting for Jule to come back from Anna's house across the street. Anna Holt was the girl he dated then, the eldest of three daughters of a German family who had been our neighbors for as long as we had lived in our house. Our silence while we waited was imposed by our knowledge of Mother's disapproval of Anna, not as a young woman but as a "sweetheart" for her son. For one thing, the War had been over for less than a year, and we were still not prepared to look upon German-Americans with unqualified approval, or forgive them for the sins of their fatherland.

Father was more rational about the matter. "Fred Holt" (the name had once been Holtz) "was born in this country. So was his wife. They're not to blame for the Kaiser."

But maybe Mother was looking for something to disapprove of in any girl Jule might have taken an interest in at the time. "I don't care, I think she's too old for him" (Anna was nineteen, Jule eighteen) "and she's too bossy. She's got her father's temperament. She's bossy and she's Catholic. If Jule should marry her, she'd make him join the Church and make all their children Catholic, and I don't want to see him do that."

"Well, he's not married her yet, so settle your feathers," Father said with his usual impatience of Mother's complaints.

"But she's set her cap for him. It's easy enough to tell that."

"Well, he's just a boy. I don't think he's ready to get himself married yet."

"That's just the trouble, Anna is the strong-willed one. She'll talk him into it if he isn't careful."

"Let's cross that bridge when we come to it." Father got in the last word because Jule was running back to us now.

"Did you kiss her goodbye?" Grace asked him with a little girl's teasing boldness, only to draw forth a dignified silence from Jule, who pretended not to hear. He settled himself in the driver's seat and backed the car out of the driveway, and we were on our way, waving goodbye to our neighbors.

The town was just waking. The streets, the houses, the store windows, the big billboards on the highway leading out of town all had a vacant, unused look about them as they waited for the day to begin. Dew still clung to the grass, and morning mists were lifting from distant pastures.

The engine of our car sounded like an intruder in the stillness of the dawn. For a long time, no one spoke.

At the beginning of every journey, there is the possibility that the traveler may never return; and so, familiar faces and objects take on a spectral objectivity with the realization one may never see them again. I could already anticipate what homesickness would be.

Our first stop was in the city of Wichita, where Mother's people lived. The trip was about a hundred and forty miles from home and took us the entire morning. Wichita was one of the two biggest cities in the state with a population then of about fifty thousand. Mother visited here frequently, coming on the train, to see her mother and her sister Patsy, and her two brothers, Uncle Jay and Uncle Tim. Grandmother was an aged widow, eighty-three years old, who made her home with her children, spending three months of the year with each. She seemed a grim woman to me when I was a child, and I looked forward to her visits to our house with mixed feelings; for, although she always brought Grace and me a bag of horehound candy or sometimes big red and white peppermints, she could be sharply disapproving of our behavior and had had the heartless honesty to tell us both, when I was only three years old, that there was no such thing as a Santa Claus, and she had "no idea why grown-ups put such nonsense in children's heads."

She was a thin, wiry woman, with burning eyes, and a square jaw, and lips which she kept pressed together in a thin, unflexible line as though to resist sensuality. When she arrived at our house for her annual visit, she would kiss each of us children dutifully on the cheek, and we would feel the dry brush of the whiskers on her upper lip. Everything about her was dry and wrinkled and aged.

I can still remember her sitting in the bay window of our living room, with windows that looked out onto the street, in a rocking chair with a table beside her on which she kept her sewing which she was always willing to put aside if I wanted to sit on her lap and let her tell me stories. She had been born in London and was full of stories about her childhood there, which she wanted to tell, I suppose, for they brought her childhood back to her and let her remember she had once been young. The stories were like fairy tales to me for I could not believe that Grandma had ever been a child and played with other children as I did. Many of her stories involved a boy named Hezakiah, a playmate who was given to mischievous pranks for which he was always getting punished.

She had a repertoire of stories about Hezakiah, some of which I begged to hear over and over again. "Pshaw, Joey! You don't want to hear that one again, do you? I've told it now a thousand times."

"Please, Grandma, tell it again. Just once more."

She could not have been without humor, as I remember her now, and yet I have no memory of her ever laughing.

Once Treva brought home a copy of *Photoplay* magazine that had a picture of a beautiful actress on the cover. Photographs were never used for magazine covers then. It was a portrait by one of the leading illustrators of the day, perhaps Harrison Fisher or James Montgomery Flagg. He had portrayed the actress with a wide and perhaps pointless smile that gave her the appearance of being the happiest woman alive. Grandmother had never seen a moving picture and prided herself upon it. She picked up the magazine which Treva had left on a table and looked at the cover puzzledly, as though trying to decipher a code. "What's that foolish hussy grinning about?" she asked me, "with her mouth spread from ear to ear."

I had never heard anyone criticized for smiling. I tried to defend the beautiful actress. "You wouldn't want her to frown, would you, Grandma?"

"She doesn't have to frown, but she should look serious. I've never found much to laugh about in this life." She didn't even open the magazine. She put it back on the table where she'd found it and never glanced at it again.

She suffered from rheumatism and would sit with a black shawl around her shoulders to protect her from drafts. She also suffered from eczema on her hands and always brought with her a strong-smelling liniment to relieve the itching. She bought her eyeglasses at the five-and-ten cent store, and she wore a set of false teeth which did not fit perfectly and rattled in her mouth at times like dice. Once

I saw her teeth in a glass of water on a table by her bedside, and they shocked me as though they were something obscene.

She still had not accepted her widowhood, and used to sit in the bay window, her head dropped onto the back of the chair, her strong, bony hands clutching the arms of the chair, her face lifted upward with the eyes closed tight, her lips pressed together, as though trying hard to contain within her the grief that flooded her heart. If Mother was with her, she would moan, "Oh God, Bess! Why don't I die?"

"Now, Ma, you don't mean that," Mother would scold.

"I mean every word of it. I've lived past my usefulness, Bess. I want to die."

"Ma, you mustn't say things like that in front of the children."

"Why not? Aren't children supposed to know about death? Are children supposed to think we live forever? Are children supposed to think there's no sorrow in the world?"

"They learn soon enough, Ma. I don't think we have to tell them."

In Wichita, we had dinner (the noon meal was *dinner* in the Midwest, the evening meal *supper*) with Aunt Patsy. She had been expecting us and had been cooking all morning, which she didn't much enjoy for she was not a domestic woman. Left to herself, she would have lived on pigs' feet, chicken gizzards, dill pickles and catfish. For company she had a few specialties she could always depend upon: she was expert with biscuits and custard pies, which we knew we would always have at her table. She admitted openly she did not like children, so Grace and I always felt unwanted when we had to visit her. We could have had dinner at either of Mother's brothers' homes, but Mother was closer to Patsy (whether or not she liked her more) and Grandmother was staying there at the time, so Patsy had to face her duty to feed the five of us. It was an ordeal for her. After we left, she undoubtedly went to bed for the afternoon and left the dishes until the spirit of industry moved her to clean the kitchen. Sometimes she was not so moved until all her dishes and cooking utensils were dirty and piled into the sink and on the drainboard and the kitchen table, and she had no choice but to clean up or throw them all away and buy new ones. Her husband, Uncle Merlin, had never been known to make any complaint about the vagaries of Patsy's housekeeping. He was a sweet-tempered man who loved her so devoutly he could never see anything she did as wrong or unpleasant. He was a dentist, a small man, always neatly groomed, who wore a nice cologne and kept his fingernails highly polished and trimmed. He was a soft little man without being effeminate, and always so patient with his wife's childish nature, so considerate of her whims, Mother said he must have been a saint.

During their entire married life (they lived into their

seventies), he continued to bring her presents as if he were still courting her. Some of the presents were extravagant ones, too: a gray squirrel coat, a red fox furpiece, two or three diamond rings, French perfume, and luxurious lingerie for her bloated, middle-aged body. But she had few places to wear her finery, for they had no friends; Patsy hated her brothers and their wives, and scorned all her neighbors as "snoops." Only an occasional Shrine festivity could bring them out into the world (Uncle Merlin was a potentate), or perhaps the appearance of a celebrated actor or singer in the Civic Auditorium, or a movie with Mary Pickford, or Douglas Fairbanks, or Norma Talmadge. The two of them lived together like lovebirds, totally dependent upon each other for love and companionship except when Grandmother was staying with them; and Patsy guarded her mother jealously, resenting the time the old lady spent with Uncle Jay and Uncle Tim.

She tried to persuade Grandmother to make her home there "where Merlin and I can look after you, Ma. You shouldn't be traipsing about at your age, from one house to another. Besides, you're not happy with Jay and Tim and you know it. Those wives they've got are goddamned harpies and they make your life miserable."

"Now that's not so, Patsy. Thelma and Agnes are very good to me. Now quit nagging me, Patsy. I love my sons just as much as you, and I'm not going to neglect them."

"Well, I don't think they love you, Ma. No son who really loves his mother would let his wife speak to her the way Thelma spoke to you that time when you stopped up the plumbing in the toilet. You were sick at that time, too, and ——"

"Now, will you stop it, Patsy!" Grandmother would become cross. "Thelma had reason to be upset. The water spread all over the bathroom floor. Now, she wasn't cross with me. She was just upset. Now, I don't want to hear any more of your talk, Patsy. You're a mischief-maker. You always have been. Even when you were a little girl, you were always running to me with stories about Jay and Tim. I don't know why you can't make peace with your own flesh and blood. They're both fine men and you should be proud of them."

Patsy would never be proud of either of them, but she knew when she had said enough. She'd keep silent a day or two before renewing her attacks.

Mother was the only member of her family who had children. This was a deep grievance to Uncle Jay, who felt that he had failed his responsibility to his Maker. Patsy liked to criticize that "Thelma's so pukey pious, she probably won't open her legs for him."

Mother made her hush. "That's not so, Patsy. Jay told me they had both tried very hard, that they both have prayed to God for a child."

"That's Jay for ya," Patsy snorted, "he thinks prayin' to God brings babies."

Tim might have been a father but he and Agnes did not

get on well, and were divorced several years later, and Tim didn't marry again until he was much older, to a woman who had passed her change.

Patsy never made any comment about her own childlessness, and probably had no room to criticize Thelma for prudery, for all of Aunt Patsy's bawdiness found its release in talk. She was probably just as shy of genuine sexual feeling as she accused Aunt Thelma of being. A few years later, when Valentino appeared on the silent screen, stirring women's hidden sexual longings all over the country, Aunt Patsy felt herself personally affronted by the man. I remember her studying a photograph that Grace had sent away for, enclosing twenty-five cents worth of stamps in her envelope, a picture that Valentino had autographed, showing him with a smile that seemed to mock Aunt Patsy's disapproval. "Bess, I don't see how you can let little Grace keep a picture like this. It's . . . it's obscene." But the only possible obscenity was in the implication of Valentino's smile, full of white teeth, and the taunting eyes. "Why, he might as well be naked."

Uncle Merlin was opposed to Valentino, too. He was trying to get together a group of his lodge members to sign a petition protesting the showing of his films in Wichita. "That damned foreigner is corrupting our women. They oughta send him back to Italy. The dirty wop."

Despite his disapproval of Valentino, Grace and I were especially fond of Uncle Merlin because he seemed to enjoy children and know how to entertain them. By hobby, he was a magician, and would often perform some of his magic tricks for Shrine shows. Aunt Patsy was very proud of him at these times. "He should have gone on the stage. He's got more talent than anyone I've ever seen at the Orpheum."

Sometimes, she would get into her spangled evening dress and assist him in some of his acts. "Merlin says I dress the show for him," she said, not without pride. "We were a big success at the Shrine Circus last year. I was wearing my purple velvet, and we did the stunt where he puts me in this box and saws it in half. No one in the audience ever caught on. Some of the most influential women in town came to me afterward and carried on about how I ever came out alive. They all said I looked very stylish, too. One woman said I looked just as pretty as Claire Windsor."

Uncle Merlin would always entertain Grace and me with his parlor tricks, with coins, or matches, or silk handkerchiefs, making them disappear and then finding them again in some unlikely place in the room or on our persons, baffling us completely. We would beg him to show us the secret of his tricks, but he kept them to himself as something private.

If Aunt Patsy ever felt any maternal longings, she never admitted them. "What in God's name does anyone want to have children for, Bess? I don't see how you stand it, having those screaming kids around you all day."

"If everyone felt that way, Patsy, the world would end."

"Well, let it," she'd say, with more bitterness than she

would ever admit that she honestly felt toward life. "I don't give a shit."

Patsy's language was something all of us in the family had come to accept, as one accepts a friend's bad breath or bad table manners. Mother would try to prevent her from speaking thus before us children, but there was a demon in Patsy that she could not control, and a perversity that compelled her to commit all the indiscretions she was ever scolded for. Her language was a secret vice, like that of some housewives who were given to drinking vanilla extract in the privacy of their homes. She was cautious enough with company to suppress this demon and to try to act like a lady, but she was never happy in the role and never very convincing. Every time she returned home from "a Shrine affair," she would kick off her shoes, let out her corset, releasing the rolls of flesh that had accumulated around her waist, and at the same time, give release to the captious spirit she had been restraining inside of her for longer than was comfortable.

"I don't know why I bother to go to those damn bridge parties. They're a bloody bore. I'd rather stay home with the cats than listen to Lula Hamilton talk about her *precious* grandchildren all afternoon, or Mayme Stilwell talk about her trip to Europe, and brag about those Paris dresses she got. They look like rags to me. I wouldn't wear them to a dog-fight."

Uncle Jay was a disciplined, self-educated man who was so repelled by his sister Patsy that he avoided coming to her house except to see Mother, whom he liked. Tim avoided her, too. "She's a troublemaker, Bess," he'd confide to Mother. "She calls up Agnes and tells her stories about me. *Dirty* stories that just aren't true. I don't care if she *is* my sister, I'm not going to have anything more to do with her." But both Jay and Tim dropped in to see us and say hello while we were dining.

They knew we were only stopping en route and didn't have time to come to their houses for a visit, so they condescended to enter Patsy's front door, after swearing they never would do so again. Their visit was brief and cordial, and Patsy, with Grandmother at her side, managed to live up to her role of hostess for the fifteen or twenty minutes of the men's stay.

She even pretended to be hospitable with some conviction. "I wish you and Tim could stay and have a bite of dinner with us, Jay," she addressed her elder brother with an unnatural sweetness, for she respected Jay even if she did resent him.

"Thanks just the same, Patsy, but you've got a crowd here and Tim and I both have dinner waiting for us at home."

"Give Thelma my love. Give Agnes my love," Mother told them.

Both uncles gave Grace and me a quarter apiece and

talked briefly with Father about business conditions in Wichita, and told Jule he was becoming "quite a man," and then left, reminding us we were always welcome to stay at their houses for a visit.

"Yes, you're welcome at their houses," Patsy said after they'd gone. "Thelma and Agnes both'd poison your coffee if you got a spot on their carpets."

The maternal longings that Aunt Patsy denied, she indulged on Grandmother, who was becoming more childish with age and more in need of pampering attention, and on every stray cat that came begging at her back door for a little salmon. The cats lurked through the house like spies, always a dozen or more of them, sponging off Aunt Patsy's gullible generosity. She bought the finest canned salmon for them, and fed them rich milk and leftover chicken, in return for which they ripped open the sofa cushions like carcasses, and shredded the upholstery on all her chairs, and she never seemed to mind. She was not careful about training them, either, and the odor of their dung sometimes sickened the members of our family, taking away our appetites at the dinner table.

Once Aunt Patsy had owned a little dog, a black and tan terrier she had named Fritz; but she had seen him killed, run over by an automobile when he once got away from her and went running into the street. We could not mention Fritz without making her cry. "Oh, God, he was such a sweet little puppy. That son-of-a-bitch that killed him, if

I had him here now, I'd drive hot pokers up his ass. I swear to God, I would."

She turned her affection to cats with the faith that they could be depended upon to take better care of themselves, for she didn't think she had the courage ever to go through another tragedy like that of Fritz. But it was an irony that the cats never returned her love, and would claw her fleshy arms when she tried to caress them, and jump to the floor to escape the indignity of her affection. All through dinner that day, they clung at Jule's feet, begging for attention, as if respecting him for hating them. Patsy was as hurt and jealous as if her husband had betrayed her.

"So the Grand Duchess Treva drove out to Colorado with the Murrays," Aunt Patsy couldn't resist saying to Mother before we left. She hated Treva for Treva, like her uncles, would never visit Aunt Patsy unless family duty made it necessary. "It's too bad about her. She shoulda been born into the Vanderbilt clan; then she could have felt at home with her own kind."

Mother made no comment. Jule snickered.

It was a relief to get away from Aunt Patsy's. She could be as entertaining as a clown, but there was always an inquisitiveness about her that threatened trouble, as if she were constantly preparing evidence with which to defend herself against some suspected enemy, and she kept trying to persuade Mother to share her hatred of Jay and Tim. "They're out to get all of Ma's money," she kept warning Mother. "They're going to do everything in their power to persuade her to leave you and me out of her will, and she's going to die soon, Bess. We may as well face it. She's in her eighties now and can't last much longer. Thelma and Agnes keep after the boys to get every cent out of Ma they can. They're bitches. I hate them both. They'd both kick Ma out of their houses in a minute if they didn't know she was going to leave them some money. Tell Ma you agree with me, Bess. Please. You don't know what they're like because you don't live here and see them as much as I do. But you're older'n me and Ma's always respected you, and if *you* tell her what Thelma and Agnes are really like, she'll believe you."

"Thelma and Agnes have always been very nice to me, Patsy. I can't tell Ma something I don't know is true," Mother would try to reason with her.

"What do you mean, you don't know it's true? You've heard the stories I've told you, haven't you? Do you think I'm lying? That dirty bitch Thelma said horrible things to Ma when she stopped up the plumbing. Ma came home to me and cried. I saw her cry whether she denies it now or not. She's just forgotten. Her memory's slipping. She forgets how those bitches treat her."

Mother would despair. Patsy would cling to her with her recriminations, trying to force them into the craw of Mother's belief. "Now stay a while longer. You don't have to go yet. There's a lot more I've got to tell you. You've got all day to get to Garden City. It's only two hundred

miles. You'll be there for supper. Now listen to me a minute, Bess . . ."

"Patsy, we've *got* to go. We don't want to have to be
driving after dark if we can help it. We've *got* to go,
Patsy." And finally we would squirm out of her hold on us,
like her cats, and relax from the pressure of her coaxing.
It was like ridding oneself of a burden to be free of her.
"She's my own sister, but I never did understand her. I
don't think I ever will," Mother said, as Jule was finding
his way out of Wichita.

3.

THE TRIP OVER the plains of western Kansas was a long monotony. The only event of interest was our coming upon Clint's Cadillac, an hour or so outside of Wichita, parked at the side of the road. Clint, with his sleeves rolled up, was changing a tire; Treva and Mrs. Murray stood by watching. Treva was a little irked that we had come upon them in the humiliation of having a flat, but Jule rose above the temptation to gloat and helped Clint. The change took only a few minutes, long enough for Treva to tell us of their shopping expedition in Wichita, and the "beautiful dress that Mother Murray bought me at Woolf Brothers," and the chicken salad they had had for luncheon at the Hotel Lassen. Treva was so embarrassed to have a relative like Aunt Patsy, she had never mentioned her to Clint and Mrs. Murray, and dreaded the day when she might have to introduce them. "She embarrasses me so, I could just die, Mother. I don't see how she could possibly be related to you and Uncle Jay and Uncle Tim. She's *vulgar*. She's *common*."

I had never seen western Kansas before. The flat emptiness of the land was awesome, and the heat was so intense it was like an indictment from an Old Testament God. The heat was dry, though, and hot desert winds kept our bodies dry. The earth itself, being so barren, one was made more aware of the immensity of the sky, the shifting movements of the wispy clouds, the drama of a black hawk soaring like silent evil, not even moving its wings. I must have felt for the first time, the mystery of Nature and the wonder of what I could not then recognize as infinity. All afternoon, I stared at the endless space.

One of Mother's greatest fears was of storms. When she was a girl in western Kansas, she had been caught in a cyclone that had lifted their house like a kite from over her family's heads and sent it crashing to splinters on the ground. Ever since, she had trembled at a flash of lightning, and feared thunder like the call of doom. Whenever there was a storm she would herd all of us into the basement of our house like a mother hen sheltering her chicks, even if the storm came in the middle of the night and she would have to frighten us out of our beds. Only Jule would resist her pleas to save his life in the basement. He was a sound sleeper and would barely rouse to consciousness when she pulled at his blankets and cried, "Jule! Jule! There's a terrible storm. It's going to rip the house apart. Come, Jule. We're all going to the basement. Hurry, Jule. Don't stay here another minute." He would grunt and go back to sleep.

All afternoon, on our way to Garden City, Mother kept watching the sky for signs of a storm. "It's almost like you wanted one," Jule said, for Mother was fascinated by her fears. "I wouldn't mind a good storm. It might cool this blasted heat."

Mother wouldn't even permit a joke about it. "Jule, don't say that."

No storm happened. The sun stayed relentless in the sky all afternoon, and our throats were like dry sponges that kept us sipping ice water from the big Thermos bottle we had brought in preparation.

"Now don't drink too much of it or will make you sick, children. Just a few sips. We don't know where we'll be able to find water again." Mother had a cautioning for every move we made in life, for every function we performed.

Father had told Grace and me that we might see coyotes on the trip, but we didn't. I was disappointed. We saw numerous prairie dogs, though, darting in and out of their holes, stopping suddenly, standing on their tiny haunches, surveying the world about them with anxiety. Once we saw a snake in the road ahead of us, but it was not a rattler, only an oily black snake that made its way to the ditch before we got to it. It is probably unnecessary to mention that Mother feared snakes, too, as much as storms.

Jule drove the entire distance, all day, not allowing

Father to relieve him. "I always feel safe with Jule at the wheel," Mother purred, sitting proudly beside him. "Even when we're going fast."

This wasn't entirely true, for whenever Jule got the car up to sixty, Mother became apprehensive. "Jule, don't you think we're driving a little fast now?" He'd smile and slow down for her, but not for anyone else. "It's not that I don't trust your driving, Jule, but we might have a blow-out, you know."

But Father would get angry. "Now look here, you young pup, cut down on the speed. We're not racing to get there. We've got all day."

I since have come to recognize something Mother must have felt with Jule at the wheel. There are some drivers who induce a feeling of ease in their passengers, just by their mastery of the machine, as if it were a part of themselves they were manipulating; whereas there are other drivers, who, although not reckless, always seem at odds with the rhythm of the motor they are trying to command, who operate without coordination, whose turns are awkward and stops are jerky. Jule drove with grace and intuitive judgment, even in the most threatening circumstances or on the most precipitous roads. Mother would have been fearless on the road to Hell, if Jule were driving. With anyone else at the wheel, even Father, she would sit up straight, watching fretfully every turn the car made, and give constant warnings and advice. "Slow down now.

Don't you see that car ahead?" "Here's a turn, don't go so fast." "I smell something burning. Do you suppose there's anything wrong with the engine?"

And Jule loved to drive. The automobile was new to civilization then, but my brother had adapted himself to it as if it were a newly evolved extension of his own body. And he loved speed, the feeling of power the steering wheel gave him, the false conviction that one is thereby control- ling one's own destiny. He longed to drive in races. He wanted to compete. He knew he could win. He longed to fly an airplane, too, and begged Father to give him the money to take lessons from one of the men, most of whom had been pilots in the War, who were going about the country giving demonstrations and advertising for stu- dents. But the future of aviation still was not foreseen by ordinary people, and Father condemned the whole business as "damned foolishness," and Mother came close to hysteria every time Jule mentioned flying a plane.

At sunset we all became quiet. The sky now dominated everything, the earth itself appearing humble and poor, its grass and foliage already seared by the burning sun, the soil dry and hard, not knowing when it would ever receive again the blessing of rain. As we looked to the west, there was nothing of man's creation between us and the horizon. Occasionally, a ramshackle farm or shed. Nothing on earth seemed of the slightest consequence; but in the sky, some- thing important was happening. Day was being destroyed by coming night, and the burst of orange in the sky was like a final flush of blood in the body's system before a being passes away. I have seen many prairie sunsets since that time, and they have always moved me to believe that there is something going on in the sky much bigger than man himself; that man's presence upon the earth is an incidental gift that we must make the most of while it lasts, even though our strivings, our creations, our sins and our virtues are all lost in infinity.

It was still light when we reached Dodge City, and Father told Jule to drive down Front Street. There he showed us the structural remains of "the wildest city there ever was." The buildings looked innocent of the barbarous sins they had housed in the past. Now they were occupied by insurance offices and real estate companies and a Mexican restaurant. Then Father showed Jule the way to Boot Hill where all the nameless cowboys had been buried, young men with no identification on them whatever, known only by nicknames like Hound-Dog, or Big Tooth, or Skinny Dick, who had been killed in senseless quarrels over a woman or a gambling debt.

One woman was buried here, too, her tombstone naming her only as Crazy Kate, or some similar name. She was a prostitute in one of the gambling casinos who had got killed in a jealous fight with one of her competitors over the love of a pretty cowboy. My father knew all the lore of "Wicked Dodge," as it was known in the days before law brought order to the rebellious town.

This was the beginning of the Great West, the edge of what once had been called the Great American Desert. People here still lived with vivid memories of Bat Masterson, Wyatt Earp, men who had been forceful in settling the country. Legends of the criminals and killers of the era still could provoke fear in the hearts of all the peaceful souls who now had made compromises with civilization. The day of Dodge's raw humanity was gone, never to be revived except, a century later, in wholesome television shows which we could not have anticipated at this time, which could safely romanticize the past.

Before the century turned, Dodge City was one of the most important towns in the nation, for it exported live beef to Chicago and Eastern cities, where it was butchered and dispatched to other populated centers. It was a small town ("too big for its boots," the saying was) and could not help but flaunt itself in lawlessness. A town of wild and arrogant men who meant to live as they pleased, and would not be stopped in their willfulness except by men who were nimbler with a gun than themselves. A wholly male world in which women could live only as whores or servants, in which man could boast of himself as an animal and piss in the middle of the street if he felt like it, despising female disapproval. Needless to say, such a civilization had to pass; crime did not cease entirely in the area but it lost its prestige, and the criminal could no longer boast of his misdeeds but was forced to hide from the law in disgrace. Crimes of violence now were rare, but when they happened, they cast a spell over the citizens, recalling to them the fearful days when the desperado had his way, when evil ruled the land, and evil was male.

There was little here now to suggest to the stranger the violence or the romance of the past. The temperament of the people seemed as level as the flat horizon. Men stayed home and minded their wives, or met downtown at the billiard parlor and drank near beer, or at the Elks Club to play cards, or gathered at the bank corner to speculate about crops and weather. Women ruled the town. They had become the guardians of public safety. Men now behaved themselves in order that their wives could walk down the street without being offended or assaulted. With the coming of law and order, it was as if men had finally given up and let their wives take over, as if admitting they had done a bad job of things and were willing now to be good little boys. But I since have wondered if their gesture was not more pathetic than noble, for all the older men I saw about me as a boy seemed to be living with a sense of guilt; no longer able to live as outlaws, they could no longer live as men.

Jule was excited, driving through the streets of this once lawless town. All the stories Father passed on to him from his own father kindled Jule's imagination, and he sought to relive the past in fiction stories and the movies of William S. Hart.

"I wish *I'd* been alive here then," he said before we left Dodge.

"Now, Jule," Mother cautioned, "you wouldn't want to be an outlaw, would you?"

But I don't think Jule answered.

Garden City was fifty miles farther on. It was nine-thirty when we arrived there and drove into the driveway of Aunt Claudia's house. We referred to it as *her* house because she was my father's sister and so seemed closer for reason of being blood kin. She was a totally different kind of woman from Aunt Patsy. A dutiful churchgoer, a diligent housewife, and a good cook. She was the youngest in my father's family, and he retained a protective attitude toward her that Mother was a little jealous of, sometimes accusing him, "You're not nearly as thoughtful of me as you are of Claudia." But this was not the time for family bickering. Mother and Aunt Claudia embraced each other when they met, and Aunt Claudia extended herself in every way to make our brief visit enjoyable.

They had already had their supper when we arrived. "I didn't know for sure *when* you'd get here," Claudia apologized, "and everything was getting cold, so we waited for you just like one pig waits on another." This was one of the most dependable jokes in the family repertoire, and could always be counted on for a laugh, everyone acting as if he had never heard the saying before.

Grace and I had never met this branch of the family. Uncle Ned was a lawyer and earned quite a good living. It was taken for granted that one day they would be rich.

Ned Jr., our cousin, was now a boy of fourteen, husky for his age, and considered himself already a cowboy, wearing boots and chaps and a Western hat. Aunt Claudia took us all out to the kitchen and fed us cold roast beef sandwiches with homemade catsup that was good enough to make a sandwich of by itself. There were also two kinds of pie, cake, and milk or coffee. Ned Jr. was tentative about committing his friendship to Grace and me, regarding us suspiciously at first, as possible trespassers into his family realm where he exercised all the privileges of an only child. Still, he recognized his duty to be friendly. In his cowboy clothes, he seemed a fictional figure to Grace and me, and he stood around the kitchen looking at us as though trying to figure out how fate, or circumstance, had ever related us to him. He would have liked to make friends with Jule, but Jule, at eighteen, was aloof to his juniors.

Slowly, Ned Jr. brought himself around to accepting Grace and me, perhaps as his charges during the time of our stay, and to acting as our big brother in Jule's place. It was like a sudden decision to extend himself when he came to us and asked, "Would you like to see the rodeo tomorrow?"

We never saw rodeos in eastern Kansas. I had never heard of them. I looked dumb, but Grace was enthusiastic. "Oh, I'd love to, Cousin Ned." She liked him already.

"You go, too, Joey," Father urged. "You'll enjoy it."

That night Mother felt so happy, and so free of fear and apprehension, to be on a vacation trip with all her family, she was able to drink an entire cup of coffee at supper and still get a good night's sleep. This was unusual. Mother had a nervous addiction to coffee. She loved it more than any other food or drink, but it overstimulated her to the point of keeping her awake all night long.

"Why don't you just let it alone if it bothers you that way?" Father would bark at her impatiently when she walked the floor at night, trying to work off the coffee's effect on her nerves. He forgot or saw no similarity between Mother's craving for coffee and his late brother's fatal craving for alcohol.

"Oh, I'm a fool," Mother would berate herself. "I knew when I was drinking it, this would happen. Oh, if my heart doesn't stop pounding this way, I fear I'll die."

"You're not going to die," Father would answer impatiently, "unless you scare yourself to death. If you can't sleep, just lie down and relax. You'll get to sleep eventually."

"Oh, I can't lie down. I can't rest. I wasn't born to rest. Why did I do it? Why? Why?"

Once at a big church picnic, Mother had drunk two or three cups of strong coffee, in the excitement of being with a crowd of friends, and then suddenly had become so ill that Father had to take her home and call a doctor. Dr. Oates appeared at the house a little before midnight, carrying his little black bag, and sat at Mother's bedside, giving her a mild sedative, rubbing her wrists soothingly and talking to her with fatherly wisdom. This happened before I was born. I only heard the story later. Mother was still in her twenties when it happened, and was fragile and pretty. "Why can't I drink coffee like other people do? It doesn't affect my husband this way, or anyone else in my family. I love it so. Why does it have to hurt me this way?"

"Because you are obviously different in your makeup from other people, Mrs. Hansen. Coffee is a strong stimulant. Some people pass off its effects without even feeling them. They are people who perhaps do not have a very keen sensitivity to stimulation of *any* kind. But you respond very keenly to life, don't you?"

"I don't know what you mean, Dr. Oates."

"I mean," he continued, "you are very moved perhaps by a beautiful sunset, aren't you?"

Mother admitted she was.

"Or by lovely music?"

"Oh, I am. I heard Mme. Galli-Curci once in Wichita and I was so thrilled by her singing, I got goose bumps. Honestly. And my sister Patsy sat right beside me and didn't feel a thing. She said she'd as soon listen to a screeching parrot." The memory amused her and she could even smile. "I was ashamed of Patsy, my own sister. We had gone to the same concert, but I heard something beautiful and she didn't. I always wondered what made us so different."

"You see, you have a keener reaction to the beauties in life, so you must also accept the fact that you have a keener sensitivity to its pains and occasional ugliness. Just as Mme. Galli-Curci's singing gave you a brief insight into the world of grace and beauty and perfection, a feeling that lifted your heart and strengthened your hope for survival, so now, a jangled nervous system, that is going to quiet down momentarily, gives you a feeling of panic that all is wrong with the world, just because you cannot drink coffee as you see others do, and enjoy its warming flavor and the lift it gives to one's feeling of well-being."

"It never bothered me this way when I was a girl," Mother argued on her behalf as if by debate she might win over the harm that coffee did her.

"We change, Mrs. Hansen. Our bodies change. Our minds change, as we grow older. You mustn't waste time regretting that you are not made as some others are, but accept yourself as you are, with your keen sensitivities and your weaknesses, too. You must stop drinking coffee, Mrs. Hansen. You must stop."

"I'm beginning to feel very relaxed now, Dr. Oates. What was that little pill you gave me?"

"There's no need to tell you. It's harmless if I give it to you on rare occasions, but I'll not give you a prescription for the pills. If you ever call me again in this condition, I shall have to let you endure your agony and get through the night as best you can."

"I promise, I'll never touch a drop of coffee again, Dr. Oates."

"I'd rather you didn't promise me that now. Wait and see."

Sometimes Mother would be able to go without coffee for two or three weeks at a time, and this would give her confidence in her willpower. But eventually, she would succumb to its rich odor in the percolator, and pour herself just a small amount in a cup, and sip it very slowly, savoring each sip with the relish of something forbidden. Or sometimes, she would pour a little in a cup and then fill the cup with hot water, hoping that if she diluted it enough she wouldn't suffer its effects on her nerves. Falsely confident that she could drink coffee again like other people, she would increase the amounts she poured into her cup and then become sick again, sometimes vomiting the bitterness it left in her stomach, or making her head pound and reel.

"Oh, God, why am I such a fool?" she would beg of the sky for some explanation of her human weakness.

In the morning, Aunt Claudia fixed us a big breakfast of waffles and sausages, coffee of course, and Mother was able to drink it again without harmful effects. It was her first return to "Garden" since she and Father had moved away, and her excitement must have fed upon the coffee's stimulation and saved her nerves. She was eager to look up all her old neighbors and friends. She wanted to visit all over town and see all the people she had known as a girl. She wanted to live again a part of her youth that was still sweet in her memory. Jule gave the morning to her, driving her wherever she wanted to go, while Aunt Claudia stayed home and prepared our dinner.

Father had a brief, brotherly visit with Aunt Claudia in the kitchen. There were some softly muttered regrets about their own brother, Julian, after whom Jule had been named, for at the time Jule was born, Uncle Julian was a handsome young man with a promising future, he and my father running the department store their father had left them, the only big store in this newly developed country. After Uncle Julian's miserable death, however, at the age of thirty-two, my parents seldom mentioned him before us children, as though trying to ignore any possibility that Jule might end up as his uncle did. This was a thought that would make Mother shudder, and that made my father apprehensive about Jule's occasionally rebellious nature. "Where do you think he went wrong, Brian?" Aunt Claudia would ask my father, sometimes with tears in her eyes, as if hoping to find an answer that would justify the tragedy of her brother's untimely death.

"I don't know, Claude," he'd always reply with a mournful nod of his head. "There was something in him, I guess, that just wouldn't settle down."

"But he had so much to live for. Everybody loved him.

He could have married any girl in town. He was handsome and smart as a whip."

"I know, I know," Father would admit mournfully, "but he just couldn't stay away from that damned booze."

The rodeo turned out to be a small neighborhood contest held in a vacant lot, participated in by Ned Jr., and some of his friends. Ned rode a young bronco, and stayed on the required number of seconds. I didn't know much about horsemanship, but Grace was impressed. She was only ten and so she realized that she could not aspire to the affections of a boy of *fourteen*; and she had also heard that it was wrong for cousins to marry. Thus, she kept her liking for Ned Jr. pretty much to herself and denied it absolutely when I tried to tease her about being in love, which always makes persons ridiculous in the eyes of children.

We left the next morning, getting another early start, prepared to make it to Colorado Springs by nightfall. All morning, as Jule drove, Mother reminisced about her visit in "Garden." "Oh, I'm so glad I dropped in to see dear Mrs. Otis. I was so fond of her when I was a girl. I wish you'd gone with me, Dad. She's so sick now, she could hardly recognize me. It was an awful shock to see her so old and feeble. When my family lived right next door to her, she was very spry. Morna says she can't live. It's awful to think I'll probably never see her again. Oh, sometimes it's painful to go back and see how people have grown old and changed. I wonder if I looked as old to some of my friends as they looked to me. Helen Kress, for instance. So fat and gray. And she was one of my best friends. Oh, time is so cruel to us."

When we got into the mountain country, and the car started climbing, Mother became apprehensive. The climb was gradual and steady. Driving now began to challenge Jule and he relished it. Sometimes the mountain roads were very narrow, and so circuitous that I began to feel nausea, and so high that Mother wouldn't let herself look down. Several times, though, Father and Jule would insist on stopping in order to get out and see the view.

"Come and look, Mother," Jule urged her, "you've never seen anything like it. You could drop the entire city of Wichita into the canyon and never see it again."

Mother braved it once, getting out of the car to stand by the roadside and see the view, but the beauty was so vast, it frightened her. "I could never have conceived such enormous space," she gasped. "I could never have conceived it."

When we arrived in Colorado Springs late that night, we stayed at the Antlers Hotel. The next morning, we drove to see the house that Father had rented for us. It was an old frame house, in good repair although it needed painting, with a wide veranda and a wide, green lawn, enclosed by a wrought iron fence. It looked inviting, very much like our house at home. Our landlady lived next door in what was called, at the time, a Hollywood bungalow. A trim little house, new and freshly painted. Father went to the door and rang the bell. He was greeted by a rather attractive, middle-aged woman with red hair who wore a great deal of makeup, Mother thought. She was officially friendly.

"Welcome, Mr. Hansen. I'll get your keys."

Then Father signaled to the rest of us to get out of the car and come with him. The redheaded woman was not our true landlady, inasmuch as she did not own our house, but was our landlady's daughter. "Mama's getting old," she explained, "and leaves the running of things to me." She unlocked the door to our house and bade us enter, Mother first. Mother had not been feeling well that morning, and she looked a little wan as she strolled from room to room downstairs. All the rooms were large and airy, with large windows that framed their views of the surrounding mountains. There was an enormous window in the living room that we all admired, that looked out on Pike's Peak. At the top of this window was a decorative, horizontal panel of varicolored glass in a floral design, almost like a church window. This panel filtered the sunlight into bright colors in the room. The carpets were nearly threadbare, and none of the furniture was attractive, most of it being heavy pieces of what was called Mission Oak. The walls were covered with a dark paper that had aged like stone. The doorway between the living room and the dining room was hung with a beaded curtain, long strands of bright glass beads that came within an inch or two of the floor. The beads rattled together when one passed through them. In the dining room was a chandelier of Tiffany glass (which had been out of fashion ever since the War) that hung over the table. Sitting in a corner was a big vase filled with cattails. The kitchen was spacious, all white, with a large iron wood-burning range that dismayed Mother.

There was no gas in the house. Father complained that this had not been told him when he signed the papers for the house, but the redheaded woman (Miss Salsbury) could only shake her head regretfully and profess she was sorry. "But I've never built a fire in my life. How am I going to get breakfast every morning when . . . ?"

But Jule, as usual, was the one who pacified her. "It'll be all right, Mother. I'll build the fire for you every night, so all you'll have to do in the morning is set a match to it."

"But I've never cooked this way before. Ma did when I was a little girl, but I didn't realize anyone cooked this way any more."

Miss Salsbury regretted she could not be helpful.

When we all went upstairs to see the bedrooms, Mother had to let Jule help her. She was about to swoon. "I can't imagine what could be wrong. I feel so weak. Do you suppose it's my heart?" she inquired of Father with a voice of helplessness.

"I'm afraid I'm going to have to sit down."

None of us had reckoned with the possible effects of the altitude. We had never before been so high above sea level.

"It takes a few days to get used to it," Miss Salsbury consoled us, although no one seemed badly affected but Mother. She had to finish the tour on Jule's arm. There were three bedrooms upstairs, all of which passed our inspection, and one big bathroom. We began to move in immediately, but Mother couldn't help us.

"I just feel so faint. I'm afraid I'll have to go to bed."

"Of course, dear lady," Miss Salsbury said attentively and pulled down the bedcovers as Jule helped Mother to the master bedroom.

"I just don't see how I can ever get used to this altitude. I'm afraid I'd better go home on the train as soon as possible. I'm sure my heart cannot survive this."

"Nonsense," Miss Salsbury kidded her good-naturedly, "you'll feel perfectly all right when you lie down. Plan to take it easy for a few days, and lie down whenever you feel you need to."

"You're right," Mother said after she had got into bed, "I feel perfectly all right now, except that I'm sleepy. I think I'll just doze awhile."

So we all moved in while Mother slept. "Let me know if you need anything," Miss Salsbury had said obligingly before returning to her bungalow.

At noon, Father called Treva at the Broadmoor. She begged not to have to join us until after the weekend, for Clinton was entering a golf tournament, and "I'm having such a good time, I couldn't bear to leave now."

By the time Treva joined us, Mother was more accustomed to the altitude and was learning to use the wood-burning stove. Miss Salsbury had left her a cookbook that listed the time requirements for cooking at high altitude. Every night, Jule filled the stove with paper and kindling and fuel, and every morning, Mother lighted a match to it and set the coffeepot on to boil.

Treva made a survey of the house as soon as she arrived and classified everything in it as "hicky." It was a long fall from the grace of the Broadmoor. She behaved like a duchess trying to make a good-natured submission to an environment beneath her. Clint drove in almost every evening to take her out dancing, or to a movie. Sometimes he took her back to the Broadmoor for dining and dancing, or in the afternoon to swim and play croquet. Sometimes he came to dinner at our house. He adored Treva, even in her most willful and headstrong ways; and when he finally did meet Aunt Patsy, he found her very entertaining, and couldn't understand Treva's humiliation.

Jule slept in the dining room on an army cot that Miss Salsbury brought over for him. Upstairs, Grace and I shared one of the bedrooms, with a screen put up between our single beds, one on either side of the room; Treva had a room of her own, and Mother slept alone or sometimes with Grace after Father returned home on the train. Mother was remorseful that Jule could not be provided for as comfortably as the rest of us, but Jule insisted he did not mind. He began to feel restless after we'd got settled in the house and there were no more chores to be done, and so he took a job in a drugstore downtown, where he could keep busy during the day and make his own spending money (he never liked being dependent upon Father); but he was always home for supper in the evening, and free to take Mother for a ride after the dishes were done, and a ride with Jule was her favorite pleasure.

Mother would always be ready to come home by nine-thirty, and then Jule would take the car alone. "Where are you going, Jule?" Mother would ask shyly, not wanting to seem inquisitive. "Are you going to call on anyone?"

"I'm just going to drive around awhile, maybe go to the pool hall. Don't wait up for me."

"All right, Jule. Have a good time." But she would never fall asleep until she heard the car rolling into the driveway and knew that Jule was safely home. She knew that he loved to drive fast when he was not with her, and she knew, too, that he had friends she didn't know and didn't want him to think she was curious about. She didn't want him to think that his late hours distressed her, so he didn't know that she stayed awake, usually until he got in. When he came in late and discovered that she was still awake, he'd ask her if she'd been worried about him. "Oh no," Mother would lie. "I've been sound asleep till just now. A dream woke me."

Sometimes at home, Father would become enraged when Jule was out late. "Where the hell *is* the young pup?" he would bellow as he paced the floor with visions of Jule careening over the town with a lot of drunken friends in the car. "If he's not home by three o'clock, I'm going to call the police and tell them they can lock him up."

"Now, Dad, please don't be angry. I'm sure there's some very simple explanation. He may have had a flat tire somewhere, or run out of gas."

When Jule would finally get in, he and Father would face each other like bulls, snorting, glaring at each other with red eyes, but after a lot of angry grumbling, Father usually had little to say but "Where the hell've ya been?"

Jule would have any of a number of explanations ready, some plausible, some not. Father would usually end the encounter with a gruff "Well, get to bed now. It's almost morning, and you've kept us up all night."

One night Treva was out very late, with a young man she had just met (if it had been Clinton, my parents would not have been worried, but this was during the school year when Clint was gone), and my father was planning to meet them at the door in his nightshirt and grab the young man by his coat collar and tell him exactly what kind of a bounder he was to keep decent girls out until one A.M. But when he heard the car drive up, and met them at the door, he recognized the young man as the son of one of his customers in a nearby town, and then all his roaring wrath was channeled into the most ingratiating hospitality.

"Well, if it isn't Smitty! Hello there, son!"

"Well, this is a surprise, Mr. Hansen."

"Come right in and sit down . . ."

4.

J ULE WAS GOOD-LOOKING, and he attracted business to the soda fountain. Girls would file into the drugstore all afternoon and flirt with him when he served them Cokes. Even Treva noticed it whenever she went into the store. Treva rather resented Jule's good looks, as if they were a property only women had a right to. Mother noticed also a very pretty woman who operated the cash register. She appeared to be in her thirties.

Jule dismissed the woman casually when Mother asked who she was. "Her name is Miriam. That's all I know."

"Is she married?"

"I don't think so. I think she's a widow, but I don't know for sure. I don't talk with her much."

"She's very pretty," Mother added, as though to test his perception.

"I guess she is. I haven't paid much attention."

Whenever Grace and I dared to tease him about the girls who flirted with him, he'd get mad and threaten to spank us. I don't know if it occurred to me then, or much later, how shy a young man can be to discover that girls find him attractive.

Treva seemed to thrive on admiration from men; Jule almost shrank from being admired by women, as if physical attractiveness were an embarrassing possession. The easiest way to fluster Jule, or make him angry, was to tell him he was handsome.

Finally, Jule delivered an ultimatum to his family: "Mother, I've got to ask you and the kids to stop coming into the drugstore all the time. I'm there to work and I can't take the time to stop and talk with you all. And it's kind of embarrassing in front of my boss and everything, to have my family coming in all the time."

"I understand, Jule, I'll see to it that we don't come in, any of us, unless we have a necessary purchase to make."

So the drugstore was now off limits for Grace and me, who had been misusing our kinship to Jule to walk to the drugstore afternoons and beg ice cream cones. To keep us from feeling scorned, though, he started bringing home a bag of candy or salted almonds, which Grace and I fought over until Mother made us share them equally; and we would count them out to see that each got his rightful share.

The presence of the pretty Miriam was a disturbance to Mother. Maybe the fact that Miriam was older than Jule by at least ten years made her seem like a seductress to Mother. Or maybe she would have been suspicious of any woman, young or old, who threatened to rival her status in Jule's affection.

She discovered ultimately that Miriam was a widow and that she was known as Mrs. George Hubbell, and that her reputation in Colorado Springs was "a little shady." Mother fretted but realized that it would be undiplomatic to warn Jule about the woman, or to tell him he must not be seen with her. Now, something told her every time he was out late with the car, that he was with Miriam. The thought hurt her. She still felt possessive of Jule, even though she realized that one day another woman would have to replace her in his life, a woman he would love as a wife. Mother feared that day almost as she would fear his death.

At this time, there was an estrangement between my mother and my father which I had only a six-year-old's vague awareness of. Yet, I often wondered why I never saw my mother and father embrace and kiss each other, as I saw sweethearts do in the occasional movies I was allowed to see at the time. My father was a handsome man, but he was not affectionate; he was incapable of the tenderness that a woman has the right to expect of her husband. He never brought her little presents, he never remembered their anniversary; only at Christmastime would he think of buying her a present, and then it was usually something for the house.

I can only guess that their sexual union seemed loveless and carnal to Mother, and so she came to feel degraded by my father's animal desires. A distance grew between them. I cannot now blame my father, or think he was evil (he was not); he was only unable to love. This sounds like a damnation of the man, but I have come to realize now that many humans are similarly unable, making me wonder if, perhaps, the ability to love is not a stage of development that all men do not attain. Or maybe the native capacity to love becomes blocked in some of us because of fear for survival. Maybe wild animals are unable to love because they must fight to stay alive; maybe that was the trouble with my father. I know that when he became old and had to retire from his strenuous work on the road, he became much closer to his family and the fights between him and mother ceased almost entirely. Not until their old age were they able to live together in peace, when animal desire had gone, and when my father's daily struggle to beat out his business competitors was remembered like a waste of spirit.

Mother wanted terribly to love and to be loved in return. But efforts to find such a union with my father ended in a series of painful failures. She said the sexual act was abhorrent to her. I heard her tell, much later in my life, how she fled from him the day after they were married — the morning after their first intercourse. She was so frightened and repelled by what had happened in their marriage bed that she returned to her parents and begged them to let her stay. But Grandma urged her back to her duty as a wife, counseling her that "Men's ways are not always seemly to a delicate woman. You've got to give in to things you may not like, Bess. That's part of being married."

So Mother finally returned to the handsome man she had been so eager to love, who had so humiliated her without knowing he had done so, without knowing why she had reacted so. She eventually gave up trying to love him, and tried to content herself just to be a dutiful wife. But it was only to be expected that she would seek the love she missed from another. Jule was the first likely substitute for Father. All the attentions she had wished my father to appreciate, Jule as a growing boy quickly responded to. I hate now to call their love "unnatural" because it seemed to us all the most natural thing in the world. We all knew in our senses that Mother loved Jule more than any living creature, but we had never heard of Oedipus and never felt it necessary to give that love a name.

There was another man in Mother's life, however, whom if she did not accept as a lover, as Father often accused her of doing whenever a fight sprang up between them, she cared for very deeply. Dr. Oates had refused to give Mother a prescription for the pills that so blissfully quieted her in a panic, but his gentle way of talking to her, his tender understanding with his firmly authoritative treatment of her child's temperament brought about an addiction to the doctor himself. He was not a handsome man. But he was wise, kindly, and highly educated. Mother began to call him for every ailment, real or imagined, that she felt. First, Father objected to the bills; then he became suspicious and made angry accusations at Mother, which she sobbingly denied. But Father decreed that Dr. Oates was never to set foot in our house again, and he went to the doctor's office and told him he'd no longer be liable for the bills he sent.

Jule was a young boy at the time, about fourteen, but Mother had to make a confidant of someone, and Treva had never been very quick with her sympathies. Mother cried on Jule's shoulder and begged him to believe in her innocence, which he devoutly did. He was willing to fight his father to defend her, but she pleaded with him not to. "Let's just forget it, Jule. As long as I have your faith in me, that's all that matters."

"Mother, you couldn't *ever* do anything wrong. I'll always believe that," he swore with the loyalty of an Eagle Scout.

"That's all that matters, that my children believe in me."

One morning when Mother passed through the dining room on her way to the kitchen to light the wood fire and start breakfast, she noticed that Jule was sleeping with his shotgun at his side, on the army cot that Miss Salsbury had provided. She was puzzled. After she got breakfast started, she returned to Jule's side and wakened him. "Jule, what is the meaning of this?"

But Jule wasn't prepared to answer. When awakened in

the morning, it took him at least an hour to become intel-
ligible. Jule and Treva were the only ones in the family
who had the gift of being able to sleep late. Both of them
could have slept every morning until noon if my parents
had permitted them to. Father acted as though sleeping
late were immoral. But this particular morning, Jule had
to go to work, and so Mother forced him out of bed, surly
and inarticulate.

After he had had breakfast and coffee, she asked him
why he was sleeping with his gun at his side. Jule tried to
bluff his way out of answering. Obviously, he was embarrassed. But Mother only became more curious. "Did you
think you heard burglars, Jule? Was there someone trying
to break into the house?" Jule said no. "Then why? You
must have been alarmed at something that happened.
What was it, Jule? What made you sleep with your gun?"

Jule couldn't answer. "I have to be going now, Mother.
I'll be late for work." And he jumped up from the table
and hurried out of the house.

It is very hard for men to admit their fears.

The next morning Mother found Jule again sleeping with
his gun at his side. Now she was deeply puzzled. But she
did not try again to persuade Jule to reveal whatever it
was he feared. She fed him his breakfast and let him go to
work without a single query. She did not confront him again
until late that night, when the rest of us were asleep, and
she got up from bed and slipped into a negligee and tiptoed
downstairs, into the dining room, and sat on the cot by

Jule's side. The gun was beside him. He was awake, his body stiff with fright.

"Jule! What's wrong?"

"Don't you hear them, Mother?"

"Hear what?" she asked, although she claimed she already knew what he was talking about.

He said, "Listen. You'll hear them in a minute."

They remained still then, and soon a breeze passed through the dining room, making the long strands of glass beads clink together in the doorway curtain. Mother shuddered.

"Oh, God, Jule! Have you heard them, too?"

"Every night. I've lain here every night listening to those spooky damned sounds. I don't go asleep until I see dawn out the window."

"Shh," Mother silenced him and put a hand on his shoulder. They both sat in doomed stillness and listened to the sounds of footsteps going up the stairs, very softly, each step making its pressure on the wooden stair with the regular timing of a metronome.

"Oh, God," Mother sighed, "I didn't think anyone heard them but me." She sounded guilty, as if fearing that she had unwittingly inflicted an illness or a strange susceptibility upon her own son. "I've heard them every night and I was afraid to mention them because I thought everyone else in the family would think I was crazy. I wouldn't let myself believe I heard them. I just shivered and tried to get back to sleep, but they *are* there, aren't they? They're real. They *are* . . . somebody's footsteps."

Jule and Mother kept their secret to themselves for several days, until finally Mother couldn't contain it any longer and cautiously revealed it to the rest of us, not admitting that she believed in ghosts but only explaining, trying to sound matter-of-fact about the phenomena, how she and Jule had been "disturbed" by the sounds they heard at night. We all listened that same night, and we all heard the steps. Treva was a little puzzled by them at first, but never allowed herself to take them seriously.

"It's just in our imaginations. What else *could* it be? I certainly don't believe in ghosts."

Grace and I heard them, or at least thought we did, and we felt they were "spooky," but we were too young to lose any sleep over them. Jule was the only one deeply disturbed by the sounds.

Mother tried to reason with him. "What good would your gun do you, Jule? There's nothing you can shoot at."

He admitted the gun's uselessness but said it gave him courage to know it was beside him. I had never realized that Jule could be afraid of anything.

One night Clinton came to dinner and we told the story to him. He laughed and gave us his rational explanation.

"Those noises are known to happen in lots of old frame houses like this one, Mrs. Hansen. They're made by the timbers. You see, the stairs are used all day, with people going up and down them, and at night, when they're not in use, the timber in them creaks."

Jule said nothing, but he had already classified Clinton as "one of those guys who thinks he's got some kind of a scientific answer for everything."

"But the sound of the steps is unmistakable. They sound in a very regular procession, just like someone walking. And there's always that breeze through the beaded curtain, just like someone passing through it. That couldn't be the timbers."

"Well," Clinton laughed, "a person's imagination can trump up all kinds of scary sounds, I guess, if he lets it. It could be a real breeze shaking the beads. I don't know. But I sure wouldn't let it bother me."

Jule later expressed himself about Clinton's explanation. "Let him say what he wants, but he hasn't been here and heard them."

Father made light of the sounds, too, when he came out in August to spend his two weeks' vacation before driving home with us. We told him about the sounds, and he listened to them the first night he arrived. He was obviously puzzled by them when he got up the next morning, but he wasn't willing to believe they were anything more than what Clinton had told us they were, creaking timbers. So we continued living with the night sounds for the rest of our stay in the rented house. They continued to disturb us

and frighten us at times, but we endured them as phenomena we could neither understand nor get rid of.

A day or two before we left, Mother summoned courage
to speak to Miss Salsbury about them. She had taken me
with her over to the bungalow, to return a few pieces of
tableware Miss Salsbury had loaned us for our stay. It
was the only time I ever visited inside the bungalow. I
was fascinated by a tiger-skin rug on the floor, with fierce
teeth and bright glass eyes that I took for real. Incense
was burning in the lap of a small Buddha. It was a Sunday
and Miss Salsbury was resting from her busy week, driving
all over the town in her little coupé, selling real estate.
She was neatly groomed in a Japanese kimono, and wore
her usual rather theatrical makeup.

Before we left, she asked us if we had enjoyed our summer. "Oh yes. Of course. It's been a lovely vacation."

"Has the house been comfortable, apart from the old
wood-burning stove, which I do apologize for?"

"Oh yes. Very comfortable," Mother answered, "except
that . . ."

Miss Salsbury waited.

"Well, I do feel a little embarrassed mentioning it, but
we've heard sounds at night."

Miss Salsbury was immediately interested. "Sounds?
What kind of sounds, Mrs. Hansen?"

"Well," Mother continued a little cautiously, hoping not
to be taken for a fool, "almost every night, we hear the

sounds of footsteps coming up the stairs. My son Julian is a little superstitious. He believes they're maybe ghosts."

Again Mother smiled and laughed a little apologetically to show that she really didn't take it all too seriously. But Miss Salsbury saw no humor in Mother's story. She became very solemn.

"We never call them *ghosts*, Mrs. Hansen."

Mother realized now that she had unknowingly broached a very serious subject with our landlady.

"You've never met Mama, have you, Mrs. Hansen? Come and meet her. Yes, bring the little boy, too."

She led us into a bright sunroom where an old lady sat in a big wicker chair, a knitted shawl around her shoulders, just like my grandmother always wore, reading the Sunday newspapers through silver-rimmed eyeglasses. Her daughter treated her with the respect of a devoted servant. "Mama!" The old lady looked up at us. "Mrs. Hansen says they have been hearing footsteps on the stairs at night."

"Well, that's interesting," the old lady replied without the least surprise.

"She says her elder son is very aware of them, and thinks they're *ghosts*."

Whereupon the old lady laughed with the kindly amusement a high priestess might feel for the naïve misconceptions of a novice.

"Let us show them respect by calling them *spirits*, Mrs. Hansen."

Mother was incredulous to find the woman serious about the matter, so serious that she could even laugh about it, for Mother herself had not yet dared to tell herself in so many words that the footsteps she and Jule were so disturbed by were actually ghosts, or spirits. She was awed by them, but she had not yet given them a name.

"And your son is frightened of them?" the old lady wanted to know out of the merest curiosity.

"Well . . . we've been . . . I guess you'd say *puzzled* by them. Yes, puzzled."

"It's amazing that they still come back, isn't it, Mama?" the daughter said with the distant compassion of a nurse for departed patients.

"Oh, some of them *never* give up. Never," the old lady spoke with peaceful regret. "But there's no reason for anyone to be afraid of them. They're lonely creatures, but harmless."

Mother felt excluded from the intimacy of the conversation, as if they were discussing a serious matter with a viewpoint particularly their own. She humbly admitted, "I . . . I guess I don't understand."

"I am a medium, Mrs. Hansen," she announced and then looked at Mother as if waiting to see her reaction. There was none. Mother only waited to hear more. "Rather, I *was*. I don't practice any more. It's too wearing. My daughter and I held many séances in that house, before we built our little bungalow."

[75]

"You mean, you call forth spirits from the dead?"

"Oh, I wouldn't flatter myself to that extent. There's not much 'calling forth' to be done. The world is *full* of spirits, Mrs. Hansen. Just waiting for us to receive them."

Mother must have shivered a little.

"There are spirits in every house, but most of us are not aware of them. I think every house is haunted, which is not a word I like but which I'll permit myself to use here for an easy clarity, *haunted* by some part of us that we leave on earth, some unrealized hope, some mournful regret, some unholy longing, some unhappy love that we can't take with us."

"I see," Mother said meekly and grabbed my hand as if to cling to a member of her familiar world, and hurried out of the bungalow with me, back to our haunted house.

When we returned home from Colorado Springs, we had proud stories to tell those of our neighbors who had remained in Kansas all summer long and endured the impersonal sun, filling the earth with its cruel heat with no concern at all for the innocent humans who had to suffer it. For weeks afterwards, Mother could talk spiritedly about the trip, telling about "those dangerous mountain roads we drove on . . . it makes your head swim to look down . . . but I wasn't a bit afraid. Oh, my son is a splendid driver," she would say, forgetting entirely her intense fear of ever taking the trip, as though now it could be regarded as just some awkward, foolish misunderstanding that could not be held against her as cowardice (for Mother's fears embarrassed her). There were stories, too, about the footsteps. "Isn't it strange? My son is not afraid of a living thing, but he was actually afraid of ghosts. Can you imagine Jule being afraid?"

5.

THE FIRST THING Jule did after piloting the dusty
Buick into the driveway was to take a long stretch and
then hurry across the street to see Anna Holt, even before
unpacking the car. Mother was a little impatient with him
but kept silent. We all entered the house and opened the
windows to let out the stale air. What a pleasure it was to
be home again, to enjoy the familiarity of our house as
something new. Mother called the grocer, the newspaper,
the milkman, the iceman, to tell them all to start delivery
again.

When Jule returned a little later, he spoke to Father.
"I've got a date tonight. Can I use the car?"

Father said it would be all right.

"Charlie Chaplin's on at the movie," Grace begged, "why
don't you take us?"

"I want to go, too," I whined.

"Take them all to the movie, Jule. You know how they
love Charlie Chaplin."

"Mother, I've got a date. I don't see why I have to take the brats along."

Grace and I began to cry. Charlie Chaplin movies were one of our unquestioned rights, like a half-dollar for taking castor oil.

"Oh, take them, Jule. You can bring them right back after the movie lets out if you want to be alone with Anna."

"I don't have a date with Anna," he announced in a matter-of-fact way he had long since cultivated to avoid drama in family arguments. We all looked dumb.

"Didn't you just come from Anna's house?" Mother asked.

"Yes. But she wasn't there. I've got a date with her sister."

"With Maureen?" Mother had to force every bit of information out of him.

"Yes, with Maureen."

"But, Jule, she's just a child."

"She's sixteen," he replied.

"Even so, Jule, that's awfully young. Wh-what happened to Anna?"

"Nothing's happened to Anna," he replied. "I've just got a date with Maureen. That's all. I don't see any reason to have a family conference about it."

It was clear, he didn't want to talk about the matter any more. We had to accept his change of affection as unquestioningly as a change in the weather. When Mother and

Father saw Maureen again, they realized what had happened. The summer months, while we were gone, had matured her into a young woman. She was extremely pretty. And there was a sweetness about her that Mother had to admit liking.

"If only she wasn't a Catholic."

That night, Jule took Grace and me to the movie with himself and Maureen, and brought us both home immediately afterward and deposited us in the house and returned to the car to take Maureen for a ride. Their desire to be alone was very mysterious to Grace and me. That was a night in late October. One night the following October, when Father was home, Jule had to beg for the car.

"Cars, cars, cars. That's all you young people think about today is *cars.*"

Humility was not one of Jule's everyday virtues, but he summoned what he was capable of for the plight he seemed to be in.

"*Please*, Dad. It's very important I have the car tonight."

"Well, you be in early, you young pup, or you'll not get it again in a long time."

"I'll be in early, Dad. I promise."

He was willing to promise anything at that moment.

By two A.M., Jule was still not home, Father was pacing the floor again, chewing a cigar butt, making his usual threats. The telephone rang. It was Mrs. Holt. Mother talked to her.

"We're sick with worry. Maureen has never been out this late before. Where has your son taken her?"

Mother apologized, but promised Mrs. Holt that Maureen was safe if she was with Jule. "My son is a good boy, Mrs. Holt. And you have nothing to fear when your daughter is with Julian."

But Mrs. Holt was not so trustful. Father and Mother argued so vehemently, even Treva woke up. So did Grace and I. We sat at the bottom of the stairs in our nightgowns, excited by Jule's daring in staying out so late. A little before three o'clock, after Father had called the police and Mrs. Holt had called the police, we heard the family car come slowly into the driveway. Father had the door opened even before Jule and Maureen got to the front steps, but he had not expected Maureen to be with Jule. Always before, Jule had walked her across the street and taken her to her door before coming home himself. Hand in hand, they entered our house. Father had to hold his temper, because he could not let himself swear in the presence of a girl as young and innocent as Maureen. We had all quieted down by the time Jule and Maureen stood before us, and Jule announced, again matter-of-factly, "Mother, Dad, I want you to know that Maureen and I are married."

The first effect upon both families was catastrophic. The Holts were morally embarrassed that their daughter had not married in the Church but had eloped and got married by a justice of the peace. And she had lied about her age. It was hard for her family to forgive this "sin." Jule had turned nineteen in September but he had had to claim to be twenty-one. Both families were stunned by their children's show of independence. The effect upon Mother was grievous. She could not help but feel a deep hurt that her favorite of all her children, the most beloved person to her in all the world, had suddenly, without even asking her advice or giving her any warning of what was in the back of his mind, driven off in the middle of the night with a girl who was not yet out of high school, and made her his wife. It was like an insult to Mother. She had to reason with herself that Jule had not meant to hurt her. She tried to shed her tears in private.

Since the first of September, Jule had been working at one of the men's clothing stores in town. He had got the job on his own, too proud to ask Father to use his influence with any of his local customers. Jule's boss was one of the few Jewish men in town. His name was Martin Feinbaum. He was fond of Jule and gave him a generous raise when he heard of the marriage. Mother liked Mr. Feinbaum, and his wife, too. "Jews are *not* stingy," she used to say to her neighbors, "and Jewish men are always good to their wives."

The marriage ceremony was performed again at early mass in the Catholic church. None of our family had ever been in the church before except Treva, who had attended midnight mass there with friends, on Christmas Eve. It looked foreign to us, with its gilt and ivory and statues and crucifixes, like a piece of Renaissance Italy set in the middle of our little Western town. Jule was now a Catholic. Mother regretted this at first as a further breach between them. He seemed a different person to us now, kneeling silently before the richly ornamented altar, with Maureen's hand in his. There was a solemnity in the service that I had never before associated with Jule.

Father was a born salesman, and never allowed matters of religion or race, whatever his personal feelings about either, to destroy a personal relationship. He never liked the Catholic Church but he never made an issue of his feelings. He had a primitive Westerner's suspiciousness of Jews, but he liked many of his Jewish customers. Yet any Jew he did not like, he could not resist calling "that damned Jew," being unable to separate the qualities he disliked in the man from his racial heritage. There were many gentiles Father disliked, but he never felt called upon to credit his dislike of them to any religious or racial cause. They were just "ornery bastards."

Once Jule and Maureen were married "in the eyes of the Church," both families felt proud, and quickly made virtues of all the faults they had first found objectionable in the union.

"I think it's good Maureen got married young. Some doctors say, the younger people get married, the better," Mrs. Holt confided to Mother.

"I think you're right, Mrs. Holt. I'm certainly relieved

now to know that Jule's not running wild all over town in the car."

No one ever knew what Anna's feelings were about the marriage of her sister with her former boyfriend. A few months later she married a man who worked in the Oklahoma oil fields, and they moved to Tulsa.

Jule and Maureen moved into a small apartment, and Maureen quickly and capably took over her role as a wife. Both families were frequently entertained at dinner, and the young newlyweds were frequent guests in the homes of their parents. Jule was different now; there was something peaceful in his nature. His wild youth had come to rest and he was ready to grow old. He never talked any more about his ambition to drive in auto races or to pilot an airplane. He was loved now, with a love that he could return.

Love seemed almost a weakness to me then. Whenever Jule and Maureen came to our house for dinner, they would come into the living room when dinner was over, and the two of them would sit together in the big chair before the fireplace that Jule had used to occupy alone, Maureen now curled up in his lap, their arms entwined around each other, their lips nibbling at each other's lips, their bodies enfolding each other as one. Grace and I stood around staring at them and giggling, but they didn't notice. We called them "lovey-dovey" and couldn't help feeling somehow they were acting "foolish." Mother would shoo us away. "They want to be alone." And Grace and I would tiptoe into another room, full of wonder about the mysterious transformation made in people by *love.*

Later, after Jule and Maureen had gone home, with Father away too, and Treva out on a date, Mother would put Grace and me to bed and then lock up the house for the night, and sit downstairs alone for a while, trying to get used to the new emptiness in the house. Finally she would go to bed with the knowledge that Jule's room would be empty, he would no longer be there to quiet her if she got frightened during the night, that Jule was gone now and she would always miss him.

It was sometimes very difficult for Mother to accept circumstances, but she did so gracefully when it was apparent that she had to. Certainly, every fiber of her being resisted Jule's getting married, but she knew she could not admit this, even to herself; and she knew she could not let herself hate Maureen. If Maureen had been hard or selfish or mean, Mother could have found righteous justification in hating her son's marriage, but Maureen was the opposite of these things, soft and generous and sweet. That made the marriage harder for Mother to bear; she knew she had to love Maureen, or try. I don't know if she ever came truly to love her, or accept her as one of her own; but she tried so hard, I think she may have finally succeeded.

Jule's marriage had been only a minor social event to Treva. She was enjoying her own life so much, of which

Jule had never been a part, that she felt no absence when he was gone. She was fond of Maureen and thought her a "perfect wife for that wild brother of mine," but she was never very interested in visiting them or having dinner with them. She was always out with Peggy or Nan or Betty, or going to parties in the homes of her friends who had already married. She was probably a little relieved, too, that Jule was no longer at home to shame her for taking other dates while Clint was at school. It was the first year of the Twenties and Treva was living her life as if it were her undisputed right to enjoy it. Father refused now to give her the spending money for the clothes and accessories and fineries she liked, so she took a job in an exclusive little dress shop called Ogdens whose owners, Mr. and Mrs. Ogden, were among her social acquaintances. It was an unusual shop for a small Kansas town, but there was wealth enough in Freedom and the surrounding towns to make it a profitable business venture. Twice a year, Mrs. Ogden went to New York to buy the finest merchandise she could find for her customers, and occasionally she and Mr. Ogden would go to Paris together and bring back original creations from the most noted couturiers. Treva loved her job and the Ogdens were proud of her.

If Father had been home during the week, he probably would have objected, as Jule did, to the number of dates Treva had with other young men when she was wearing Clint's big diamond engagement ring and pearl-studded fraternity pin. Mother never told my father, for she knew it would start a fight between him and Treva, and Mother would do anything to avoid discord in the family, except when a clash between herself and Father was unavoidable. But Mother felt remiss about Treva's carefree behavior.

"Aren't you afraid people will talk, Treva?"

"What about?" Treva answered defiantly.

"Why, you're dating other men when you're engaged."

"I'm going to have a good time, Mother."

"But there *is* some gossip, Treva. You know there is."

"I don't *care*," she said with a snap of her fingers, "that much for what people say."

"But what if word ever gets back to Clint?"

"I'm not the least concerned. I write Clint almost every day and I always tell him everything I do. I've done nothing to be ashamed of and he knows it."

Accustomed as we were to the assortment of young men who periodically called for Treva after dinner to take her somewhere for the evening, we were all intuitively aware the first time that Frank Bradshaw came to the house that he was a man Treva would not forget after two or three dates, with just a name on a few dance programs to remind her of him. He was twenty-five, the oldest man Treva had ever been out with. He came from Minneapolis and had graduated from the University of Minnesota, and had been a lieutenant in the Navy during the War. He was in town on an important job with an oil company. He made a high salary. His work kept him in the open all day and his face was leathery. There was a toughness about him that did not prevent him from being a gentleman. Whenever he came to call, he was perfectly groomed. He was so hand-some, we were in awe of him. And there was an authority about the man that gave one the feeling that he was not to be trifled with.

Treva had always had her way with Clinton Murray and the other young men she went out with. They were all young men who treated her with the respect she felt she had a right to expect from them, a respect which she sometimes took advantage of without expecting to be faced by the dishonor of something she had done. If she told one young man that she was not feeling well in order to get out of going someplace with him when a more attrac-tive engagement turned up, she expected him to regard her misdemeanor, if he found out, as a girlish vagary that was not to be taken too seriously. If she sometimes hurt a young man's feelings, she never realized it, for she did not take any of her relationships too seriously and would have been very surprised to find that the young man did. She believed only in the world of manners and social graces, which could always be manipulated to accommodate her; the world of deep and vulnerable feelings was not real to her then.

Treva had met Frank Bradshaw at a country club dance. He was a new man in town, a friend of Betty's or Louise's, she had forgotten which, and all the girls at the party were attracted to him, buzzing about him when they got together in little groups between dances, or in the ladies' lounge at intermission when they were powdering their noses. He had danced with Treva and asked her for a date. She had accepted. He called for her at nine o'clock the first time, ready to take her on a hayride. He was wearing a leather jacket and corduroy riding pants, and laced boots, like Jule had used to wear. Treva was never downstairs when a date arrived for her. Out of intention or careless-ness, she always kept him waiting at least ten minutes. So, when she did make her appearance, hurrying down the stairs, "I'm terribly sorry if I've kept you waiting," it was with the aura of an actress timing her first appearance on stage. This time Frank Bradshaw smiled at her patiently, as if forgiving a child, and took her outside where the hay wagon was waiting, full of their noisy, high-spirited friends. He must have said something to Treva about not liking to be kept waiting, for she was always ready thereafter, when he came to call, looking a little submissive.

Frank Bradshaw became a nightly caller, appearing for Treva in tailored suits or a tuxedo, ready to take her some-where in his Stutz roadster. But he was never in a hurry to leave. He would sometimes hold their departure while he sat on our big mohair davenport, Treva beside him, and talked with us, telling us about his experiences in the War, or his travels in Europe after the Armistice. He told us something of his work, too, supervising the laying of a pipe-line for one of the new oil companies that had sprung up in the area. Sometimes he would hold me in his lap and ask me if I played a good game of baseball, making me wish that I did in order to have his admiration. Many nights he would bring a box of Martha Washington chocolates that Treva would generously give up for Grace and me to fight over; or a big bouquet of roses that Mother would put in a vase to adorn the living room for a few days. If there was a circus in town, he saw to it that Grace and I accompanied him and Treva, scoffing at Treva if she objected to having to "drag the kids along." Frank seemed to enjoy us. At Christmastime, there were presents for us, too. We all came to like the man so much, and to admire him so reverentially ("He's such a *manly* fellow," Mother would often say after he had left the house with Treva), that it was difficult for Mother to remind Treva of her promises to Clint.

Being in love did not become Treva. It saddened her spirit. She no longer came running down the stairs when she was going out for the evening, smiling like the actress's picture on the cover of *Photoplay*, talking fast and excitedly about all the little affairs that crowded her day, shrugging her shoulders irresponsibly if Mother reminded her that she should go visit Mrs. Murray more often, or that she should write her Uncle Jay a thank-you note for the lovely birthday present he had sent her. The entire momentum of Treva's life changed. She always looked somehow pensive now, and there was an uncertainty in her actions. When she was alone with the family, she seemed listless and sad; in Frank's presence she appeared almost defeated.

"What are you going to do?" Mother confronted her one night when she was not going out because of a cold.

"What about?" Treva couldn't even face the question.

"Treva! How can you ask that? You must know what I mean. You're in love with this Frank Bradshaw."

"What makes you say that?"

"Why, Treva, it's written all over your face. Don't you realize it?"

"Well, what if I am?"

"It's perfectly all right with your father and me, but what will you do about Clint?"

"I don't want to talk about it, Mother. Please. Let me alone."

It was a lucky coincidence that year that Frank returned to Minneapolis for the Christmas holidays when Clinton was returning home for his vacation. Treva was spared the ugly predicament of having to choose between them for dates for holiday parties. She had written Clint about Frank Bradshaw but without admitting that she was probably in love for the first time in her life. Probably, she didn't even admit how much they saw of each other. But, of course, the town had been gossiping about her, and word had got to Mrs. Murray that "Treva Hansen is out every night with that Frank Bradshaw," so Clint, when he arrived home for the holidays, asked for some explanations. Apparently, Treva gave him answers that satisfied him, for they attended the holiday parties together; and by the time he was ready to return to Dartmouth, he and Treva were convinced again that they would marry the following June. She was even prepared to tell Frank Bradshaw when he returned from Minneapolis that he mustn't call her again.

When he did call her, shortly after the first of the year, Treva's promises to herself and to Clint lost all substance in her memory. "I'll be ready, Frank," she said humbly over the telephone, and that night he was at the house again, with flowers, ready to take Treva out.

"I think you're more in love with him than you are with Clinton," Mother said. "Does Frank want you to marry him?"

"Yes," Treva admitted, as if wishing he did not in order to spare her the pain of making a decision.

One night, that winter, they had a fight. Frank had brought Treva home late, after Mother and Grace and I were in bed asleep. We were awakened by their angry voices in the parlor, a sound that brought back memories of the savage fights that Treva had had with Jule, and again I heard an angry male voice calling her "a bitch." And again, there was the smarting sound of her flat hand slapping his cheek, and then the sound of his hitting her in the face and of her body falling to the floor.

"You're a dirty little cheat," we heard Frank condemn her. "I don't take that kind of treatment from *any* woman.

You've been lying to us both. You're a worthless little bitch."

Mother was standing at the head of the stairway in her nightdress wondering if she should interfere. Grace and I both lay awake in our beds, staring at each other across the room in which the light shone from the upstairs hallway. Then we heard the front door slam, and the roar of the Stutz's engine, and the sound of the car starting off with a jerk and speeding away, the tires crying as they skidded around the corner. Then the sound of Treva sobbing, running upstairs, slamming her door behind her.

"Treva! Treva! Let me in," Mother pleaded outside her door.

"Go away!" she sobbed. "Go away!"

The next morning, Treva told Mother that she would not be seeing any more of Frank Bradshaw. "I *hate* him. He's mean. He's overbearing. He's cruel. I wish I'd never met him. I hope I never have to see him again."

A few weeks later, Treva was to leave for Paris with Mrs. Ogden. The invitation from Mrs. Ogden had come as the gladdest surprise, Treva never having expected it. Mr. Odgen, who was staying home to take care of business, explained that he had been to Paris before and was content that Treva replace him. Treva felt a great favor had been bestowed upon her. She looked forward to seeing Paris with all the excitement one might expect of a provincial girl, only twenty, going abroad for the first time. It was excitement enough to help her forget Frank Bradshaw for a while.

Of all the children, Treva was the only one in whom Mother never indulged her hypochondriacal fears. This was perhaps because Treva being the firstborn and acclaimed by her grandparents and uncles and aunts as partly their own, Mother was never allowed to feel as richly possessive of her as she was of the rest of us. If it had been Jule or Grace or I who had been going to Europe, even at Treva's age, Mother would have been creating storms at sea for us, or some kind of shipwreck disaster like that of the *Lusitania* or the *Titanic*, which were still fresh tragedies in the public mind. But she always had calm confidence that Treva could take care of herself in any situation; she never invested Treva with her own nervous sensibilities.

A few days before Treva was to leave for New York, Frank Bradshaw came into Mrs. Ogden's stylish little shop, with its thick carpets and French furniture, and Hattie Carnegie dresses on headless models, and lingerie and sophisticated perfumes. Treva told me this story many years later. She was unnerved at seeing him and tried to hide, but she could not very well, without creating a scene for the customers to gossip about. The only thing she could do was ask Mrs. Ogden if it was all right if she left for a few minutes to have a Coke. She and Frank went to the Candy Kitchen across the street and sat in the back booth where they could speak softly and not be heard. All he wanted to say was, "I think I'll always love you. I'll probably be gone from here by the time you get back. My work is almost finished. But I'll write you from time to time and let you know where I am. I think you love me and don't realize it. I think you'll have a hard time forgetting me, too."

"I'm going to marry Clint." Treva spoke with assurance. "I know I'm doing the right thing."

"All right, but let me tell you something. I want you to know *why* I love you. I've been around women who've got twice the class you've got. I see through you. Don't you understand that? And I still am crazy about you. I like something very ordinary about you that you're afraid to admit is even there. I'm in love with something *common* in you that you're ashamed is there."

Treva froze. His candor, as well as his love, was insulting to her. "I'm going to marry Clinton Murray. I have to be getting back to the shop now. Thank you for the Coke. Goodbye."

She started to get up and leave, but he held her by the hand for a second longer. "All right, but just remember how I feel in case you ever change your mind."

Treva knew she would never change her mind. She ran out of the Candy Kitchen and back to the shop and refused to let herself think of Frank Bradshaw for years to come.

But Treva didn't get to Paris until much later in her life. The night her boat was to sail from New York, Mother got a telegram from her saying she would return home on the next train. Mother supposed that Mrs. Ogden had canceled their Paris trip, which everybody in town considered a foolishness anyway. She arrived over a weekend when Father was in town to drive to the depot to meet her. She had come back alone.

"Where's Mrs. Ogden?" Mother asked.

"She went on to Paris," Treva replied in a tone that guarded against further questioning. But Mother was too curious to let the story end there.

"What happened? Why did you decide at the last minute to come home?"

"We had a disagreement. That's all. I don't want to talk about it any more, Mother. Please!"

Treva did not go back to work at the shop. It was April. In only two months, Clint would return and she would marry him. Frank Bradshaw had left town by this time, and she was free to devote herself to her trousseau and to wedding plans. She spent a great deal of time with Mrs. Murray. Clint already had a job waiting for him in the oil fields around Houston, Texas, where he was to get experience before going to work in an office. They were to have a honeymoon first in California. The wedding invitations were sent out early in May and immediately presents started arriving which Treva would put on display on a big table in the parlor: silver, china, crystal, linen, electric waffle irons, electric coffee percolators. Every day, some new surprise would be unwrapped for the family to admire. Getting married appeared to Grace and me a much better way of getting presents than even Christmas.

Before Treva left on her honeymoon, she explained to Mother, feeling distaste in even talking about the matter, why she had not accompanied Mrs. Ogden to Paris. "She wanted to sleep with me." Mother was astounded. "The first night in New York, she tried to persuade me to let her get into bed with me, and I said, 'Pearl, it's just a single bed. We'll not be comfortable,' and she said, 'Oh yes we will, Treva darling.' I had the most peculiar feeling. I told her I was accustomed to sleeping alone, but that didn't stop her. She got into bed with me and started using her hands all over me, and I was so frightened, I jumped out of bed and told her please to let me alone. And then she got mad. The next day she told me she thought she'd go to Paris alone. I was relieved. I couldn't stand being around her after that night."

It was hard for Mother to believe such a story. "But she's a married woman. What does her husband think of her doing things like that?"

At this time in our culture, we did not have ready access to the words that classify sexual divergences. "Well, I think he's a little peculiar, too," Treva confessed. "He's always entertaining high school boys at their house when Pearl is gone, and lots of times he leaves the shop in the afternoons and goes over to the pool hall and talks to some of the boys there. He gives them money. Pearl knows all about it."

Mother said it was the most disgraceful thing she had ever heard of. "Why, they're both worse than poor Bonnie Sherman. They're . . . they're *degenerates.* Both of them."

"Please don't tell any of your friends, Mother. You've got to promise me. Only a few people in town know about it, and I don't want to start any gossip. They've both been very good to me, and I like them. I don't want to cause them any trouble."

"Of course I'll not talk about it. It's too *disgraceful* to talk about. I want to put the whole story out of my mind. I don't even want to think about it. It simply makes me sick."

A year or two after Treva left on her honeymoon, the stylish little shop, called simply "Ogdens," went out of business. Some of the high school boys whom Neil Ogden had entertained in the game room of the beautiful house he and his wife had built on the river at the edge of town, had talked at school about their experiences until the news spread all over town that Mr. Ogden was "a pederast." The gossip about Mrs. Ogden never got outside the small circle of her friends. She divorced her husband immediately, and was given all their property and money. She left town and started a shop somewhere else by herself. No legal action was ever brought against Mr. Ogden, perhaps because the boys he was attracted to either were homeless or from very poor families who were in no position to feel outraged by their sons' associations with the man. But his social fate was worse by far than that of Bonnie Sherman. Former friends would not even speak to him. He was a total outcast. His face now was always unshaven, his clothes unpressed, as if his mere presence no longer deserved grooming. What had always seemed a native elegance in the man now became a corruption. His presence in the town was such an embarrassment that people soon stopped talking about him; it was considered unseemly and unpleasant to dwell on "morbid curiosities." Finally, at the request of the police, Neil Ogden left town. No one ever heard where he went. No one even inquired.

The day before Treva was married, she received a postcard from Frank Bradshaw. He was in South America. The card said he would be back in Minneapolis soon and that he'd appreciate a letter from her if she had the time to write. She sent an invitation to the address he gave her. She thought about the postcard for a few minutes and threw it away.

The marriage was held in the Presbyterian church and was a splendid affair. All the Packards and Pierce-Arrows and Stutzes in Freedom rolled up in front of the church to deposit the town's gentry, the ladies dressed in lace and satin, the men in dark suits or cutaways. It was an event that Treva had anticipated for two or three years with mixed pleasure and dread; this was the occasion when she would have to present Aunt Patsy to Clinton, and admit that this gaudy creature was her aunt.

"Thank God it's summer, so she won't wear that moth-eaten gray squirrel coat," Treva said, without accounting for the extremes of Aunt Patsy's tireless imagination and cunning.

She and Uncle Merlin stepped out of a new maroon Marmon sedan, with Patsy flourishing two feather boas, one pink, one yellow, hung around her neck. On her feet, black patent leather pumps with ankle straps; on her head, a kind of turban studded with great glass jewels. Uncle Merlin, beside her, smiled as proudly as if he were escorting the Queen of Rumania into the church. Upon seeing her, Treva sucked in her breath and held it until she gathered courage to face her embarrassment. People in the church stared at Aunt Patsy but she and Merlin never doubted that the stares were complimentary. But her appearance could not help but seem a mockery to Treva of all that Treva longed for in her own life. It was like a cruel reminder that Patsy could not resist making, in return for the years of snubbing she had received from Treva. It was as if the demon in her wanted to say, "Just remember that you've got *my* blood in your veins, too, Miss High and Mighty."

By September, Clint and Treva were at home in Houston. Treva sent us a picture of their pretty house. With both Jule and Treva gone now our house seemed empty to Grace and me. We missed the fights that woke us in the middle of the night, and the flowers that arrived from the florist, and the boxes of candy we had fought over, and the fresh-killed game that Jule would bring home for our table. But more than anything, we missed the two people who had created the ideals by which we would always judge men and women, whose lives would always make our own seem commonplace, whose glamour we would never dare compete with.

My mother did not miss Treva, far off in Houston, one particle as much as she still missed Jule, who had only moved to the other side of town. He was no longer *her* Jule, whom she could depend upon to take her for a quiet drive on summer evenings, and talk to her consolingly when she felt deserted, and tease her good-naturedly about her fears.

6.

A FEW WEEKS after Treva's marriage, Mother got a
telephone call one night from Aunt Patsy.

"Oh, God, Bess, Ma's sick. I'm so worried I don't know
what to do. Why don't you bring the kids and come over
here and stay with me this summer. The doctor don't
think she can last much longer, Bess. I need someone to
help me care for her."

Father drove us to Wichita the next day and left us,
Mother and Grace and me.

"Oh, Jesus, I'm glad you're here," Aunt Patsy greeted
us. "Ma's been asking for you. The doctor was just here.
It's cancer, Bess. She's not gonna get well. Oh, Bess, it
breaks my heart to see her suffer this way. The pain's so
bad at times, she can hardly bear it. I've got her in the
downstairs bedroom. I sleep on a cot beside her. You and
the kids can have the sleeping porch. It's the coolest place
to sleep. Christ, it's been hot. A man fried an egg on the
sidewalk downtown in front of the bank yesterday. Not a

breath of air. Poor old Ma. I've put the electric fan in her room. I'll buy us another if I have to. We'll get along somehow. I hope you'll do most of the cooking for me, Bess. That'd take a load off my shoulders. Ma keeps me busy every minute."

The problems and sufferings of age are never very real to children, just as the problems and sufferings of children are never serious to their elders. I was seven or eight years old at this time. Grace was eleven or twelve. And we still sought our own pleasures, although Death dwelt beside us, with animal mindlessness. There was an Orpheum Theater in Wichita that offered a new program of vaudeville every week, and a moving picture. Every Saturday afternoon, Grace and I were allowed to go just as we would have been allowed to go to the weekly Chautauqua concerts if we had stayed home. We enjoyed the vaudeville much more, for it did not aspire to be educational. I can still remember the slapstick of Al and Loie Bridge, and the chorus numbers with the stage filled with pretty girls parading in gauzy drapery as the lights softened, changing from lavender to rose to blue, while a baritone in a tuxedo sang "Lady of the Evening." And Spanish dancers, and ventriloquists, and gymnasts, and magicians. In the movies we saw, I remember Betty Blythe, and Clara Kimball Young, and Claire Windsor. After the show, we were allowed an ice cream soda. Death was never real, even though its smell confronted us every time we returned to

Aunt Patsy's house, the rank smoldering of cancer like burning flesh, the same smell that pervaded the entire city on days when the packing houses burned the inedible organs and leftover parts of butchered cattle.

Knowing now that Death was near, Grandmother no longer wanted to die, as she had used to brag, but feared the dark mystery and wanted again to live. "You're going to be all right, Ma," Patsy tried sometimes to cheer her, but she was never convincing. "What do you think I should do, Bess? Should I tell her the truth? Would you wanna know it if you were going to die?"

"I don't know, Patsy. I don't know."

"Oh, Jesus, I can't bear to see her suffer so."

Patsy now had the power to avenge herself on her brothers. She would not let them into the house to see their mother. "All you want is money," she accused them righteously when they came to her door demanding their rights to see Grandmother. "Now get out of here. *I'm* looking after Ma. She doesn't want to see either one of you."

Mother was shocked but helpless. "Patsy, you can't act this way. They've got a *right* to see her. She's dying, Patsy. She's their mother. You can't keep them away."

"Now don't you take their side, Bess. You don't know all the ornery things they've done. Tim is chasing around with another woman. I know it for a fact. He's no good. And Jay is trying his best to get Ma away from me and keep her over at his house for Thelma to mistreat. That's all he wants, is to get her away from *me.* I'm not going to let them near her."

"Patsy, what do you care about her money? She doesn't have much. Only a few thousand. Let her give it to the boys if she wants to. You've got to let them see her, Patsy."

"They'll not set foot inside this house," Patsy vowed, with a demonic spite that seemed to recall some atavistic lust for vengeance.

"Patsy, I don't want to be a part of this. They're my brothers. I love them."

"Love," Patsy spat the word like phlegm. "That's pure bullshit talk. I don't believe in it."

"Ma! Listen to me a minute, Ma. There's a few things I have to explain to you, Ma. You see, it's costing me and Merlin a lot to keep you here this way, Ma. Now we're not objecting. You know how much Merlin loves you, Ma. And I wouldn't have you go anyplace else, even if we should go broke trying to take care of you. Besides, the doctor doesn't think you should be moved, the condition you're in now. But I know you want what's fair, Ma. I know you don't want Merlin and me to go in debt looking after you. Now Merlin has arranged for his lawyer to come here this after-noon, Ma, and then you can sign your money over to us. Bess don't need it. Her husband's doing well on the road. Besides, Bess hasn't had any of the expense of looking after you. And Jay and Tim are both rolling in money, Ma. Rich as Croesus, both of them. And Tim is spending all his money on another woman. Agnes told me. She's thinking about divorcing him. He don't deserve a dime, the way he's been acting. Now the lawyer'll be here this afternoon, Ma. You wanna do the right thing by Merlin and me, I know you do. We deserve it, Ma. We've looked after you good. It's not that we think you're gonna pass away soon, Ma, 'cause Merlin said to me just the other day, 'Patsy, honey, your Mother's going to outlive us all' and I believe he's right, Ma. But just in case, huh? Just in case anything should happen we're not prepared for."

This was the whispered conversation Patsy would have alone with Grandmother, day after day, until the old lady's strength gave way, and she finally signed the will that Merlin's lawyer made out for her, and then turned over in her bed and tried to sleep away the memory of her own blood's treachery. All summer long, we stayed in Wichita, thinking that if she didn't pass away this day, she surely would the next. Then the end of August came, and the blood still coursed through Grandmother's ancient veins, and she still cried out at night, clutching the cancer's hard knot at her side.

"What's keeping her alive?" Patsy would ask Mother, looking awed. "Even the doctor can't account for it."

Grace and I had to be in school the day after Labor Day. So Father drove back to get us and we returned home. Mother, too. She could not wait for Death to make its expected move.

By some kind of miracle, my grandmother lived almost a year after we left her in Wichita, but Jule died only six weeks after our return. He had cut himself when shaving in the washroom of Feinbaum's Clothing Store, and contracted a virulent blood poisoning that took his life in three days. The infection was deceptive in not appearing to be anything serious until the day before he died, by which time his face had swollen into a freakish distortion of his handsome features, and he had become almost unconscious with pain.

There are two minds at work in us during a crisis: one mind in Mother could not imagine that this trivial affliction would end her son's life; but another mind was sufficiently alarmed to bring him home again where she could make one final claim on him before a possible death. There was not room in his and Maureen's tiny apartment for a nurse to stay, and Mother and Maureen could not stay as close to him at the hospital as they could in our home. An ambulance brought him back to us, and he was carried on a stretcher upstairs to his old room (which I vacated for him), where he lay inert for a night and a day and most of another night. There were a day nurse and a night nurse attending him every minute; and Mother and Maureen spelled each other staying beside him. They were guarding Jule's life as if they could keep death away by physical force. But Death came. It stole into the house like an arrogant thief, while Maureen and Mother and the night nurse

all were at Jule's side, and vanished before their very eyes
with his priceless breath.

There is a period of endless silence after death occurs,
before recognition sets in. The house was soundless the rest
of the night. Mother didn't seem to know what was happening when the nurse called the doctor dutifully and told him
her case was ended. Then she changed out of her uniform
and left. Father O'Neill arrived early in the morning.
Mother had begged the Holts to wait another day before
asking for extreme unction. "I know he's going to be better
tomorrow. I just know it."

Father O'Neill stayed until the hearse drove up before
the house on cushioned wheels, and two young men, one of
whom had played basketball with Jule in high school, came
into the house with solemn respect for their duty, and
placed Jule's body into a long box which they had to
maneuver down the narrow stairs with the same impersonal care they would take for a dresser or a highboy.
Then out the front door, depositing the box into the rear
of the hearse, while some of the neighbors watched from
their windows. Then the shiny black machine rolled away
like a cloud, turning the corner at the end of the block as
we all stood on the front porch and watched. Not until
it was out of sight did Maureen suddenly crumple and sigh,
"Oh, no!" clamping her hands over her face as if she had
suddenly glimpsed the depth of life's careless cruelty and

could not look again. She had been pregnant for two months. The marriage that had just begun was now ended. Mrs. Holt put her arm around her and led her home across the street.

October was still summer-warm. Mother sat on the front porch the rest of the morning, letting the hired woman clean up the room that had just been emptied. She sat there on the swing, perfectly calm, even a little sprightly, while she talked with us of everything else she could think of: a new dog in the neighborhood, the way the Medills (who lived across the street next to the Holts) were painting their house, asking Father if he had had a good business week, anything that would keep her from recognizing what had happened. She sounded just as she might have any other day, when we heard the bell in the church steeple strike twelve and she rose to her feet and said, "I guess I'd better be thinking about what I'm going to feed you kids for lunch," and then walked into the house.

Father, Grace and I still sat in silence. Then we heard Mother's shrill scream and rushed into the living room to find her fallen to the floor. She had seen the enlarged snapshot we had made in Colorado of Jule at the wheel of the Buick with Mother beside him, Grace, Father and I in the back seat. It was a picture she had had framed, and kept on the living room table where it could always remind her of the summer we had spent together in the mountains.

"Oh, my son! God give him back! He wasn't meant to die!"

But God was stern, and unrelenting. He doesn't end our griefs, Mother had to learn; He can only help us to endure them.

II

Winter People

7.

THE MEMORY of my grandmother often returns to me, of her sitting in the rocking chair in the bay window of our living room, wishing to die; of her telling me there was no Santa Claus; and asking my mother, "Why shouldn't children know about death?" For I think we all should have known about death at that time. I sometimes think that every child, as soon as he is old enough to enjoy life, should be told that it doesn't last forever, and that he should remember death every day he awakens. I think every human being, upon getting up in the morning, should look in the mirror and remind himself that, whatever pleasures and gratifications the day promises, there will be other days when his heart turns black, and he can only wish that God would quietly take him from the earth and spare him the travail of waiting for the rest of his days to pass.

There was never any thought of death in the days I have been writing about. We all lived with the fancy that whereas death certainly happened to others, something would just as certainly spare us from ever facing it; and our days on earth would be filled with happiness. I don't think any of us, as I look back on my childhood, ever were prepared for any of the hard experiences that life unthinkingly puts in one's way. Even a trip to the dentist was a misfortune we felt God should spare us.

Mother's life was consumed by grief for years after Jule's death. She could never quite accept the seeming injustice of one so young, whom she loved so dearly, with all his life ahead of him, dying so suddenly, without warning, of an insignificant little cut. Death should at least appear with reason and announce itself in advance. If his death had been fated, as in a Greek tragedy, she'd have been able to accept it more gracefully. As it did happen, it was like trickery and she couldn't understand a God who would treat her so treacherously. She had to supply some kind of reason for his death, some mystical explanation. God must have been punishing her in His mysterious way for some vague misdemeanor she had forgotten.

Surely, she could have done something to have prevented his death. She was certain, had he not married so young, had he still been living at home with her to look after him, he would have lived his life's course. She would sit for long hours brooding. The following summer, she was still brooding, sitting on the front porch swing, her face a diagram of conflicting lines and wrinkles, her mind always seeking reasons. How could her neighbors go on with their lives, even though all had paid her their condolences after Jule died and attended his funeral and mourned with her? Even now, months later, the sounds of their voices that had forgotten her tragedy and were speaking again in daily sounds, seemed disrespectful. The world should have stopped and mourned with her forever, and made some public tribute to her grief.

My driving never pleased Mother as Jule's did. I was the "baby" of the family and was never allowed to rival Jule, whose manhood, it seemed to me, had been created for him as a sacred garment. I had to fight for my own, with whatever means I could find.

When I grew older and entered high school, it was my taken-for-granted duty to drive Mother to town every Saturday morning to do her marketing. We no longer had a family car now, only my father's Dodge sedan which he used for the road, and brought home Friday night, and drove away again Monday morning. He no longer made a very good livelihood for us. Chain stores had all but destroyed the small-town merchants that men like my father sold to. The wholesale house he had worked for in St. Louis by this time had gone out of business; and my father, now in his sixties, had to look very hard for a company that would hire a man of his age. But it was known that Brian Hansen had lots of friends on the road who would buy from him, whatever house he was selling for; so he managed to get another job with a small wholesale company in Kansas City that sold a cheaper line of merchandise; and thus he was able modestly to support us.

The only extravagance in which Mother could indulge now was buying groceries, so Saturday mornings were like a holiday for her or a spree. It was the one time during the week when she had a chance to go to town and look in all the store windows and visit all the markets and talk with the grocers and their wives, looking over the produce that had been brought in from the nearby farms, comparing the prices of canned goods in various stores, taking advantage of sales or "specials." Also, she was certain to meet some of her friends while shopping, ladies she knew from the D.A.R. or from the Ladies Bazaar of the Presbyterian church. Driving her on some of these expeditions required my patience. She would feel somehow deprived if she did not get to visit all the major grocery stores in town, and she usually had two or three small neighborhood markets also in mind, that had advertised in Friday night's paper something they were selling at a bargain. I would either have to sit outside and wait for her (sometimes I brought along a book to read), or go inside the stores with her and stand on one foot and then the other while she made up her mind about her purchases or gossiped with the grocers. We would return home around noon, the back seat of the car loaded with full grocery sacks, which it was my job to transport into the kitchen. I would sigh with relief when the job was done. "You're never gracious like Jule was.

Jule never complained about helping me shop. Jule never grumbled and begged me to hurry."

Sometimes I would take her for rides, after supper, on summer evenings when the light would remain in the sky until after eight o'clock. I would drive her out to the city park, where there was a pretty road along the river, and to Monkey Island, a new addition to the town's little zoo, a small island circled by water and a wall, on which a little town had been constructed for the monkeys to live and play in. It was a popular place to visit through the spring and summer. It gave people a destination on their evening drives. We would always see friends. And we would watch the monkeys until their behavior became obscene and Mother would turn her face, saying, "Those depraved little beasts!" All the congregated ladies would look away with the pretense of not having noticed, if a monkey started to masturbate or a pair began to copulate. Young boys would snicker, their fathers shushing them or cuffing them.

Sometimes we would stop at the Dairy Farm for an ice cream cone, another place where townspeople gathered. Sometimes we would drive out to Hannah's Highway Drive-In and have her crisp fried chicken for supper, or chili and tamales, and homemade apple pie. And Mother would enact again her enticement to coffee, and take a few sips from my cup "just to get the flavor," sometimes ordering a cup of her own with simulated daring, and then coming home sick with dizziness or nausea. "I don't know why I can't drink coffee like others do. I don't know why," she would complain as though God might still set things right and grant her the freedom to drink all the coffee she wanted.

We seldom went to a movie because Mother was claustrophobic, and she hated melodrama. "There are enough sad things in life," she thought, "without seeing them in movies." Usually, she enjoyed her own fantasies more than those of the movie-makers. If there was no one to take her for a ride on summer evenings, she would sit on the porch and live over her favorite memories. Sometimes Mrs. Holt would drop over and sit with her, or Mrs. McCoy, or Mrs. Bagby, next door. Sometimes Maureen would come over for a visit, but she was married again by this time and we didn't see as much of her as we did for the first two or three years after Jule's death. There was Jule Jr., though, who reincarnated much of her son for Mother, and he had much of his father's tender regard for her, even when he was a child of seven or eight. But he was not Mother's own. Maureen and Mrs. Holt had equal claim to him. And by the time I was in my early teens, I had created a life of my own that made me a little too independent for Mother to enslave me. I had discovered the world of poetry and literature. "Your head is always in a book," she complained. And my mind was always full of what I'd read. My ears were not always listening to Mother's recital of her memories. Whenever I brought her back from an evening ride, she would get out of the car and return to her post on the swing of the front porch, like a bird coming back to its roost. "You're a good driver, Joey, but not as good as Jule. Jule was a *splendid* driver. I was never afraid for a moment with Jule at the wheel." After all those years, she had not got over the whimsical injustice of Jule's death, and she still could not help feeling a personal deprivation.

My sister Grace suffered some of the same belittling comparison with Treva that I did with Jule. Whereas Treva's numerous boyfriends had been a cause of constant concern to Mother and Father, Grace's lack of them was a matter that Mother turned into a frantic cause. "Don't be shy with boys. Learn to smile when you see some nice boy who attracts you. You need something of Treva's spirit. How *she* could have had so much appeal for young men, and you so little, I'll never understand. You're standoffish, Grace. You've got to learn to laugh with boys and talk with them about the things that interest them, and have a good time with them."

Sometimes I felt personally guilty for Grace's shyness with boys when she was in high school. She still carried a physical mar that I had inflicted upon her in my infancy. One of Treva's soldier friends, home on leave, had brought an enormous soldier doll as a present for Grace and me. I was three years old at the time, Grace eight. We fought over possession of the doll jealously. The doll was almost as big as I was. It had a big, hard-enameled head, the dough-boy's cap for which we soon lost. I once held the doll by its feet, trying to persuade Grace to kiss it, and the body of the doll fell forward from the loose-jointed legs, the head hitting Grace in the mouth, breaking off the bottom half of one of her two front teeth. Mother could not resist blaming Grace's failure to attract young men on the broken tooth, the cause for which always related back to my infant carelessness. Dental science at that time was not equipped to mend the tooth. Mother kept Grace constantly aware of it.

Whenever a young man was expected to call for Grace to take her to a party, he received a heartiness and enthusiasm of welcome that must have embarrassed him. Mother had spurred Father and me to "by all means, make him feel at home." So every boy was coaxed into the best chair, offered candy or something to eat, Mother acting at times as if she would force-feed him one of her Lady Baltimore cakes, or a turkey sandwich if the time was during the holidays. And she would talk with him engagingly about his family, if she knew them, or ask him about them with flattering personal inquisitiveness if she did not know them.

"Oh, you've just moved here from Garden City! Dad, did you hear that? This boy comes from Garden. That's where Mr. Hansen and I met. Yes. We were married there. That's where we took the fatal step. Do you know the Garveys there? Mrs. Garvey is Mr. Hansen's sister. Yes. And they have a son who must be close to your age by now. No, I guess he must be a little older. I think he's off to college somewhere now. Isn't that a coincidence, your coming from Garden? No, we haven't been back for years, not since we drove to Colorado years ago one summer. We stopped off in Garden overnight. Oh yes, the Garveys gave us a royal welcome. You see, Mr. Hansen's father used to own the big department store there. Oh, it's changed hands many times since then. I've no idea who runs it now, at the corner of Main and Second. Yes. Garden is where I spent my girlhood. I think we always retain fond memories of the place we grew up in. To tell the truth, I never really had a home until my family settled in Garden. We were like gypsies, my father trying to find a place to settle where he could make a good livelihood. My father was English, you know. Yes, he came here just before the Civil War. He didn't any more than arrive on these shores until they put a gun in his hands and told him to fight for the Union. I'm a D.A.R. on my mother's side, because her great-great-grandfather fought in the Revolution, and then her great-grandfather returned to England. Isn't that unusual? Oh, I'd love to go to England sometime. My brother and his wife have been. They've traveled all over Europe. They looked up the place where our father's family came from and . . ."

Grace's appearance could never amount to more than an anticlimax. Sometimes she wore a look of apology when she appeared, as if she were sorry for the young man who was taking her to the party. It was as though she felt she was inflicting herself on him. Mother had trained her

to smile just enough to keep the cracked tooth from showing, so her smile upon these occasions was never very confident. An invitation to a party, something that thrilled most
girls, filled Grace with dread and agony. For after each
invitation, there began a period of constant coaching from
Mother, about what she should wear, how she should
treat her date, ending up each diatribe, "God knows, I
never had to tell Treva these things. Treva *knew*."

And I remember taking Grace's breakfast to her on a
tray after she had awakened from the late sleep Mother
and Father permitted her after a party. Sometimes I
would find her crying. The matter of her popularity had
become a cause for me, too. I wept for her as, when a
child, I had wept for Cinderella, classifying all the flap-
pers at the party as ugly sisters, and praying that some
day Grace's own Prince Charming would arrive, a handsome young man who would appreciate her sweetness
and gentility. Sympathy brings us closer to people, and
helps us to learn from them. Treva had given me insight
into woman's aggression; Grace taught me something of
her vulnerability.

Before Grace left for college, a way was found of fixing
her tooth. Uncle Merlin (a dentist, too, but not a specialist
of the kind my sister's tooth required) told us about a new
orthodontist who had come to Wichita and was doing very
successful work. He made arrangements for Grace to see
the man, so Grace spent a week with Patsy and Merlin
while the new dentist put a cap on the broken tooth that

had broken so many girlhood dreams. And Grace was able to leave for the university in September with a new confidence in herself and her appearance, which was most attractive. But most of a woman's beauty is derived from her belief in that beauty. It was too late for Grace ever to achieve that belief. But she was happy at college, away from Mother's anxieties and reproaches. She joined a sorority and had dates, and did well in her classes.

Two or three times a year, Aunt Patsy and Uncle Merlin would visit us. They had long since got rid of their Marmon. "Christ amighty! It cost us fifty dollars just to drive around the block," Patsy exclaimed. Sometimes they would enter our driveway in a bright new Essex, or a Hudson. For many years Patsy and Mother would review Jule's tragedy. "You know, Bess, I think it was the Catholic Church that killed Julian."

"Patsy! What are you talking about? He died of blood poisoning."

"I'll bet all that incense they burn was what gave him that infection. There's something *foreign* about it. They send that stuff over from the old country and it's made of camel turds. You said he went to mass the morning after he cut himself. I bet anything, that damned old incense they burn got into his pores somehow and killed him."

Mother eventually tired of Patsy's harangues. It was useless trying to argue with her because she never accepted the bounds of reason in her rebuttals, and she scorned the entire world of factual information if you presented her with encyclopedic truth to prove her wrong. "Well, who cares what any old encyclopedia says? They just make up those books to suit themselves."

With demoniacal fury, she still sought vengeance upon her brothers, especially Tim, the closest to her in age. Uncle Jay, by this time, had become one of Wichita's leading citizens, president of the School Board, a prominent member of the Rotary Club, and he and his wife Thelma had been to Europe; so Jay was out of Patsy's reach. She could not hurt him. Uncle Tim, however, was having a difficult time and so was vulnerable. He and Agnes had had a fight that ended in divorce, and so Patsy befriended Agnes for the first time in order to coax out of her some of the personal things in Tim's life that she could hold against him.

"Bess, he sees this young chippy all the time. Agnes told me. A girl young enough to be his daughter. She's nothing but a common slut."

"How do you know that, Patsy?" Mother asked. "You've never met her."

"Well, I certainly *have*."

"Where did you meet her?"

"I walked up to her apartment house one day and went in and rang the bell."

No matter how long one had known Patsy, one never became totally accustomed to the shocks of her compulsive behavior. Mother was astounded. "You mean, you actually went to her home and . . ."

"Well, shit! She didn't know who I was any more'n Adam. I told her I was looking for another woman. I made up a name. She said in a kind of common way, 'I never heard of her,' and was about to close the door on me when I noticed she had a cat in the house, and so I smiled and told her how much I liked cats, and then we got to talking a little. I found out she teaches school. She teaches the second grade at the James Whitcomb Riley, a poor school on the south side of town where nothing but a lot of white trash kids go. I don't know what Tim sees in her. God knows she ain't pretty. But she's not ugly. Anyway, when I got home, I found out who the principal of that school is, and I called him up and told him that he was hiring a teacher who was no better than a *whore*, that this Geraldine Prather was running around town with a divorced man and . . ."

"*Patsy*! How could you have *done* such a thing? Why should you want to hurt a young woman you don't even know? You don't even know what's going on between her and Tim. And besides, it's none of your business, whatever he's doing."

"I did the right thing, didn't I, Merlin? The woman's nothing but a whore. And I *do* know what's going on between her and Tim. I saw them go up to his apartment one night. He lives over his stationery store now. They tell me he's not making a dime. It was ten o'clock and I stayed around until after midnight and she never came out and I saw the lights go off, so I suppose that means they're not getting into mischief together."

"You mean . . . you *spied* on them?" Mother dared to ask, fearing a truthful answer.

"It wasn't *spying*. I just think I got a right to know what's going on. He's my brother, isn't he? I've got a right to know what kind of mischief he's getting into."

Her curiosity about Tim was like the curiosity Grace and I had felt about the personal lives of Treva and Jule when we were children. Aunt Patsy was still a child. She was still trying to get the best of her brother, for some Freudian reason, to make a villain of him in the eyes of some parental figure, in this case my mother, tattling on him as Grace and I had used to tattle on each other, feeling that to put the other one in the wrong necessarily put oneself in the right. The more mean gossip Aunt Patsy could uncover about Uncle Tim, the more content she felt with her own wasted life.

No one in the family had ever confronted her with the shame of her treatment of her own mother when she was dying, of forcing her upon her deathbed to turn over all her money to herself and Merlin in her will. The entire sum amounted to only a few thousand dollars, which Mother and Uncle Jay and Uncle Tim were all willing to agree should, by rights, go to Patsy, for Patsy had spent far more time looking after Grandmother than they. But Patsy was so talented in the use of cunning, she trusted no other means of deriving what she wanted out of life. Uncle Jay and Uncle Tim never knew about the deathbed scenes, as we did who lived in Aunt Patsy's house when they happened, and could hear the soft persuasive sounds of Patsy's voice from the bedroom. And Grandmother herself in shame, had told Mother what she had done. "I don't have the will to fight her any more, Bess. I'm leaving her what little I've got because I guess she deserves it. She's looked after me good the last few years. I wish I had something nice to leave you and the boys, but I don't. There never was much, but what little there was is Patsy's. She's a devil, Bess. She's my own daughter, but she's a devil. I love her, though, because she's my own. You love her, too, but never trust her. For your own good, Bess. Never trust her."

We often wondered among ourselves how Uncle Merlin, so gentle and softly refined, could tolerate Patsy's turbulent and offensive behavior as long as he did, year after year, without ever correcting her or losing his temper. We had never known him to voice an objection to anything she did, except to say mildly, "Honey, don't you think maybe you're imagining things?" Or "Honey, don't you think you should leave your brother alone? After all, he's not done anything to harm you." But these tender corrections were never expected to stop or alter her mischievousness. But there was a period when, for a few years, he suffered spells of amnesia, and would leave his dental office forgetting his way home. He would forget his identity, too, and sometimes wander the streets of Wichita, stopping people and asking them his whereabouts, and if they could help him find out who he was. These spells did not happen often, but they terrified Aunt Patsy. "My God, Bess, is he going crazy, do you suppose? What the hell is wrong with him? I know it's not drink. Do you suppose he's just putting on?" Mother thought he should see a doctor. "Shit! Whatta *they* know?" Patsy came back sharply. "Doctors don't know any more'n you and I do."

Uncle Merlin never mentioned the spells to anyone. Eventually they passed. I often wondered if they were not the result of some inner rebellion that the man could never find courage or words to express. Thereafter, there always seemed to me something sad and broken in his sweetness; and there was a mystery about him now that made me realize that I really didn't know the man's heart and never would.

8.

AFTER GRACE WENT AWAY to the university, I was the last child left at home. Grace was in college all during my high school years, and then a graduate student and assistant in the English Department by the time I graduated. The house seemed very empty to me, with Treva, Jule, Grace, all gone. Treva wrote frequently, Mother waiting for a weekly letter with an anxiety that begged not to be forgotten. Treva's letters read to us like fiction; Clint's parents (who had moved to Houston, too) had bought them a new Cadillac; Treva herself had just bought a gray squirrel coat and a "stunning red satin dinner dress that I'm going to wear to the New Year's party at the club" or "Kitty and I are giving a luncheon party to help raise funds for the Red Cross, etc." By this time, Treva had two children of her own, a girl of six, Marcy, and a baby boy, Clinton Jr. Clint made enough money to keep them in some luxury. With Treva gone, our lives at home seemed without color and moment. Her life gave us a feeling of belonging to that brighter world of pleasure and privilege and prestige which all Americans, I suppose, feel it their right to be a part of.

I had always been a good driver, maybe as good as Jule had been, even though I had no craving for speed or to drive in races or pilot an airplane. Yet, I always drove with a steady rhythm and good reflexive actions. I enjoyed driving on those summer evenings, just to relax and feel the breeze stirred up by the car's movement; and I enjoyed, too, the feeling of driving to reach a destination, the tranquilization of one's energies all being united to reach one goal. Yet, Mother had created in her mind a legend of Jule's driving that she liked to romanticize in her memory, and she never allowed anyone to rival him. And so I grew up with the knowledge that it was pointless for me to compete with her memory of Jule. Anything I attempted that Jule had ever done was certain to appear commonplace in Mother's judgment. She felt she owed him this peerless seat in her memory.

I never went hunting, or played basketball, or smoked a pipe, or wore corduroy pants, or boots. I unconsciously plotted my life to prevent comparison with Jule. I had few friends or playmates, I didn't enjoy playing ball, or marbles, I was regarded as sort of a sissy by most boys my age, and lived my childhood years in secret embarrassment and painful isolation, as though waiting for some vagrant passion to overtake me and fill the moments and hours of my days with meaning. But I didn't know I was waiting or what I was waiting for until my junior year in high school, when I happened to read a few of the poems of Wordsworth in my English Literature class. The greater poets still had not reached me. Shakespeare's greatness was too vast, too taken-for-granted for me to see. Milton seemed ponderous. Keats and Shelley both seemed affected to my seventeen-year-old taste. But I found in Wordsworth a pastoral longing, a sad reflectiveness that touched me personally and deeply. So, very tentatively, I presumed to write poems. Then, my childhood's unhappiness, as by some magic manipulation, was cast into a remote corner of my consciousness, and I felt myself a person who dared to look to the future with expectation.

Although my driving never pleased Mother as Jule's did, Mother had come to care for me too, and to depend upon me; I did not realize how much until the morning early in September when I stood in the living room of our home, dressed in a new gabardine suit that Mother had bought me to wear at the university, my small steamer trunk packed and waiting for the transfer man to pick up and take to the depot, my two suitcases waiting beside the door until Father backed the car out of the garage. Mother had been quiet all morning as she fixed my breakfast and hurriedly ironed a couple of shirts so that I could pack them. Neighbors had come to tell me goodbye, and gone. All my thoughts were centered upon the new life I was so eager to begin, I could not stop to consider the life I was leaving. Mother and I stood in the living room alone, when she suddenly cried out in raw anguish, "I'm alone now." Her voice shook me. "You're the last of my children, and now you're going, too. You've *all* left me, one by one. And what is there left for me but to live on with a man who doesn't love me, and grow old and feeble alone, without any of the people I love to help me?" I knew nothing to say. I was beginning a life now that I had a right to. How could I stop and try to understand the feelings of one whose life was nearing its end? My mother was past sixty now. I had been born very late in her life, and she had held me an extra month in her womb as if not wanting to let me into the world, as if wanting to hold me inside her forever as proof she would always be young and fertile. For she sensed that as soon as I was born, her change would come. "How am I to live alone in this empty house with nothing but memories and snapshots of happiness?"

"Mother, do you think I should stay?"

"No. You've got to go to college. I realize that. Children are born to leave us eventually. I have no right to complain. I'm being selfish. I've lived for you children and that isn't right, for now I've no life without you. A mother should live first for herself, and then she can bear the agony of always saying goodbye."

The car was in front of the house now. Father was honking. I stood. "Go on, Joey. Get out of here. Hurry! I'm not going to the depot to say goodbye. I couldn't bear it!"

I kissed her hurriedly and picked up my bags and ran as though it was my last chance for survival.

I did survive. That life force that grows inside us and prompts us at crucial times to act for the sake of our own preservation, saved me as if from a precipice I might fall from, back into the lost world of my childhood and dreams, a world that would have coated me like a cocoon and never let me free. How easy it would have been to stay. How deeply I felt my love for my mother, sitting on the train with friends who had gone through high school with me and now were entering the university, too. I must have seemed morose during the trip, for I had never realized this love before. During the happy days of my high school years, I had taken her love for granted, and her presence at home. Now I had left a love that had nourished me all my years, that had fed me encouragement like cream, and fretted over all my wounds as if they were her own. I knew I would miss her, but I was too eager for independence to realize how necessary love can be, or to think I would ever need it.

My first year's work at the university was not distinguished. I had a difficult time with all my courses outside the English Department. But I thought I was enjoying myself. I joined a fraternity, and there were occasional weekend trips to Kansas City to see road companies of New York shows: *The Barretts of Wimpole Street*, Walter

Hampden's production of *Cyrano de Bergerac*, and the *Ziegfeld Follies*. These were new and exciting experiences for me. I also met a girl I became very fond of, Betsy Parsons, also a freshman, who sat next to me in French I. Betsy was already one of the most popular girls on campus, for she was extremely pretty, and bright and humorous. So I didn't presume to count for much in her affections. Her greatest love was the theater. She planned to major in Drama as soon as she entered her junior year, and already she was showing a considerable acting talent in the college productions. I was one of her greatest fans. It was rare, however, that she was free to give me a date. She seemed to be attracted to the good-looking football players and the wealthy "playboys" who had sports roadsters to drive her around in, and money to send her flowers and gifts. I was a little too awed by her, I suppose, to attempt any expression of physical love.

I was a member of my fraternity without being a part of it. I lived in the house and obeyed freshman training, took my meals there, slept there, but found only a couple of other members whose company I enjoyed. Still there were card games in the lounge on rainy nights, and guest nights when we were free to bring our girls or friends to dinner. And there were the parties, sometimes formal, sometimes costume, when we would pay an orchestra from Kansas City to come over and play a dance for us, and the prettiest girls on campus would be there, and we'd sneak drinks of bootleg whiskey somewhere in private corners of the house or on the grounds. We were all expected to have a few drinks at these parties even though our house rules placed a fine on drinking. It was a rule we exercised only when one of the men got embarrassingly drunk. Sorority girls had to be back at their houses by one o'clock on weekend nights when the parties were held. This requirement didn't give the men much time to be alone with their dates after the party broke up. Sometimes, after taking their dates home, they would go out on the town or even drive in to Kansas City or Topeka to find a prostitute, or "an easy lay."

Second semester, Betsy and I found ourselves sitting together again in French II. After months of friendship and, on my part, tentative courting, she sweetly accepted my invitation to my fraternity's spring dance. I was, of course, very proud to be able to tell the upperclassmen in the house that I was bringing Betsy Parsons to the party. Once I brought her there, however, the older fellows gave her such a "rush," I danced with her only two or three times. After the intermission, I didn't see her at all, until the orchestra was playing "Bye Bye Blues," and we all started looking for our dates to get them back to their sororities by closing time. Betsy finally showed up, hurriedly rearranging her hair, with Skip Holloway, a sophomore from Kansas City, wealthy and one of the most successful ladies' men in our chapter. "Oh, I'm *so* sorry to have kept you waiting, Joey honey, but Skip and I went out for a little nip and the moon was so beautiful we just forgot about the time. Please don't be mad." And she kissed me on the cheek. I ignored my pride and immediately forgave her.

When I returned to the fraternity after taking Betsy home, I found another party going on in the basement. About six of my fraternity brothers with one drunken girl, Roxie Kimble, a town girl not a student, whom any male could call at any hour of the day or night and arrange a meeting with. "C'mon 'n' join us," Ernie Stuckey urged me when he came hurrying into the room we shared to get a box of prophylactics out of his handkerchief drawer. I felt that to have refused would have cast doubts upon my masculinity, an uncertain thing at best, I feared, that daren't hide from any challenge. I followed Ernie into the basement where Roxie lay on her back on a filthy mattress that had obviously been used before for many similar parties. The room was sickeningly overheated, the furnace having been overworked to keep the house warm during the party, and there was a mixed smell of sweat and shaving lotion and reeking alcohol and tobacco. With Ernie behind me, I joined Dick Stroll, Buster Dawson, Hal Murphy, Bernie Bridges, and the others, all in various stages of inebriation, their tuxedos tossed over the water pipes or thrown into a corner, most of the men keeping on their shoes and socks, otherwise naked, their organs already standing high with anticipation. Dick Stroll was first, since he had originated the party. We all stared like bird dogs on the scent of game. The experience was a primitive rite, revealing elements of character I'd never witnessed before in the men I'd lived with in the house. But I was repelled, too. At times, I wanted to run. Pride made me stay. I felt I had to go through this, as though through some painful initiation. When Dick got on top of the girl, he jabbed inside her as if he meant to disembowel her. Sex was like an act of hatred or vengeance. "You snob fraternity bastards," Roxie cried out. "That's all you want me for is to fuck! Well, go on and fuck me. *Fuck* me, I tell ya! That's what I'm here for. Hey, there! You with the big tool, c'mon and fuck me. You with the li'l peter, fuck me. I'll take ya *all*, ya snob sonsabitches!"

When it came my turn, I had to overcome revulsion to achieve a numb orgasm. "Wipe your cocks clean, fellas," Dick said callously when we all had had a turn. "She's prob'ly got the clap."

For weeks afterwards, I was sure I had contracted syphilis, and I felt a sick guilt, as if I had betrayed myself. I had pretended to my brothers to enjoy an experience that had repelled me. I was a hypocrite. Actually, I had felt sorry for the girl I had aided in mistreating. I had wanted to go to her the next day and apologize, and ask her forgiveness. I couldn't bear to think of the humiliation we had subjected her to.

"She wouldn't know how t'act if ya treated her nice," Dick Stroll told me. "She's been on parties like that in every fraternity on campus. Ya think she'd do it if she din' like it?"

That was the only sexual experience I had ever had at that time. I didn't think I wanted another. But there were tentative, groping, unfulfilled experiences with Bob Luther, from Colorado, that I never had the courage to classify with any name. We all had to sleep in pairs in double-deck beds. Bob was not my usual bed-partner, but when winter came, some of us "turned sissy" and moved in from the outdoor dormitory to sleep in warm beds brought into the ballroom on the third floor. When I decided to make the move, Bob asked me to share his bed. Bob was a freshman in the fraternity, like me, but was a junior on campus, having transferred from a junior college. He was two years older than I. We had been good friends ever since our pledging. He was in the Engineering School and frequently had to go on surveying trips. He often went to the campus wearing high laced boots and whipcord pants like Jule. He had been raised on a ranch in Colorado in the company of men. Girls, when he got to the university, were such strangers that he felt himself shy and awkward in their presence. Bob was good-looking, strong and well made; there was always an outdoor cleanness about him that gave him something of the character of an Eagle Scout even now in his third year of college. The other men kidded him about his shyness. "Bob's afraid some girl's gonna get his *cherry*," they taunted him. I knew that his desire for girls was a constant and troubling preoccupation, perhaps the only subject that disturbed him outside of his class work, which he took most seriously.

When I woke up one night and found Bob's arm around me and his body hugging mine, I was puzzled. I cannot say that I minded or felt repelled, for I enjoyed physical closeness with a friend I liked, whose physical presence I felt comfortable in. But I thought that Bob was having an erotic dream and, in his sleep, was mistaking me for whoever the girl of his dreams might be at that time. I nudged him off me, "Hey, Bob, move over. Who do you think I am?" And grunting unintelligibly, he rolled over to his side of the bed and, I presumed, continued sleeping.

Another night, a Saturday, after Bob and I had attended a "sneak preview" of *Forty-Second Street*, all through which Bob had watched Ginger Rogers with devouring eyes and talked about her all the way on our long walk in the black midnight back to the house, we went to our bed together in the ballroom. Only a few other men were present, the exodus to Kansas City having taken such a toll that weekend. And I awoke in the early, still-black morning with Bob's mouth on mine, his breath panting, hugging me as if I were saving him from drowning, and one of his hands grabbing one of mine and holding it on his roused genitals. Instinct made me tactful enough to whisper, "Bob, what's goin' on? Are you having another wild dream?" Again, he rolled back to his side of the bed and gave no sign that he was awake. But it occurred to me that he was.

Homosexuality was anathema in our society then. Both Bob and I had seen one pledge expelled from the fraternity merely on grounds of suspicion of being "queer." And I of course still retained dark memories of the social fate of Mr. Ogden years before, in my home town.

I could not think that Bob was homosexual because he was thoroughly masculine. I supposed that an effeminate personality was a concomitant of the homosexual. I was repelled by effeminate men. I avoided them in all my classes on campus, perhaps fearing an effeminate element in myself that might classify me as one of them.

The morning after the second nocturnal episode, Bob's face avoided mine at breakfast, and he wore a look of hurt that I easily recognized was a look of rejection. I felt guilty that I had probably injured him; yet it was still difficult for me to believe that Bob could possibly have wanted a sexual relation with me. At the big table in the sunlit breakfast room that Sunday morning, he made a point of sitting on the other side of the table from me, and neither noticed nor addressed me all morning. I later forced myself to draw him out in conversation and to find some topic that we could both laugh about, just to assure him that I was still his friend and would forget any of his nighttime misjudgments. I felt I had to rescue his threatened pride, perhaps because I felt a love of him.

I never asked myself if I was rejecting a love that I might need or enjoy. I never dared tell myself that the possibility of any kind of sexual love could have existed between us. I'll never know whether it could have. I only feared that to have surrendered to Bob's awkward attempts at lovemaking would have made me feel weak and womanly. But maybe I feared the same personal degradation in any love affair. I reacted in the situation as I knew society had prescribed me. Bob and I remained friends and continued to be bedmates throughout the winter, but he never again made any kind of pass at me; and in the spring, I returned to the open dorm, sleeping with my former bedmate, a scholarly upperclassman who never had erotic dreams.

9.

WHEN I RETURNED HOME from school that June, catastrophe had stricken our house like an ancient curse. I sensed a deep disturbance when I saw my father's face at the depot. It was the face of a man unable to show his despair. By habit he tried to smile in his usual cordial way, just as he did when he entered a customer's store; but the smile, the cordiality now were empty reflexes: "Here, son, let me help you with those bags," he offered. But I couldn't let him. He looked too old and frail.

"I can handle them, Dad. Don't bother."

"No. Let *me*. Let *me*," he insisted, and took one of my bags and started for the car. I thought probably the grief I saw on his face was brought on by financial worry and the Depression, which was just now making its full impact felt in the Midwest.

"No, son. Business is not *good*, but we're managing to get by, with a little scrimping here and there. Of course, I won't be able to send you away to school again next year, but you can spend your sophomore year here at the junior college and maybe by the following year, I'll be able to send you away again. I want you to finish your education, Joe. You weren't cut out to make your living like I've always done. I want you to have your degree."

This was information he had already written me. I didn't mind the thought of going to school at home again. I could still make good use of the time, and I'd have friends at the junior college, some of the same friends who had gone away to the university with me the previous September. Something else was disturbing my father. His efforts to sound normally cheerful were pathetic, like a man with a wooden leg trying to walk as if he had two.

We drove into the familiar driveway, the swinging turn made by the car bringing back memories of the countless times over my eighteen years that I had come home. Now I was coming home again. My father stopped me before we entered the house, and his face now admitted the gravity of the situation.

"Now, son, your mother isn't feeling too well. That's why she didn't come to the station with me. I think she wants to talk with you alone for a few minutes, so I'm driving down to my sample room and do some work. I'll be back for supper."

A soft, summer rain was beginning to fall onto the streets and lawns, and the sky was dark. Even the atmosphere was preparing me for tragedy. I felt my father was deserting me, as usual, in a time of need.

As I watched him hurry back to the car, his shoulders huddled like those of a guilty man trying to get away from trouble, I knew that some crisis had passed between him and Mother that had exposed an enmity between them that, despite their sometimes violent quarrels, had never been openly admitted.

Mother stood in the center of the living room when I entered. She, too, looked much older even than when I had seen her at Easter, and there was more gray in her hair. Her little body stood rigid, her face set in an expression of indignant hurt, as though her whole being was trying to rise above some deep humiliation. I stared at her with a boy's wonder and she seemed not even to see me. I set down my luggage and went to her, taking her in my arms, aiming to kiss her as I always did. But she turned her head from me and pulled away from my embrace.

"You mustn't kiss me any more, Joey. You may never be able to kiss your mother again."

"What's wrong?" I dared ask.

"Didn't your father tell you anything on the way home from the depot?"

"No," I said, "only that *you* had something to tell me."

"Why do you suppose *I* didn't go to the depot with him? I always do, don't I?"

"Yes, Mother."

"I didn't go this time because I'm ashamed to be seen."

"Why, Mother?"

Then she posed her face before me under the light and

I saw a couple of raw little sores on her lower lip, supposing them to be fever blisters.

"Your father has given me a disease that I don't have the courage to name."

I still could not come to terms with what she was trying to tell me. We never named the disease they shared. I finally guessed.

"We are both in the treatment of Dr. Damon. It will take us two years to get rid of it. It's costing us every penny we've ever been able to save. That's the real reason we can't afford to send you back to school next year. Look!" She extended her left arm, pulling up the sleeve of her dress for me to see the blue wounds left by the doctor's needle in her veins. "Every Saturday morning, we both have to go to his office, for a while it was twice a week, and get this serum shot into our veins. I'll have to wear long sleeves all summer to hide my arms from the neighbors. Dr. Damon says the sores on our lips will soon disappear. We're both being careful about the eating utensils we use. I keep them set aside for us in the kitchen so there is no danger of anyone else using them. The doctor says the infectious stage will pass after a few more weeks, but I don't think I'll ever feel safe in kissing my children again. It's all I can do to hold up my head when I pass my friends on the street. I wish to God I could die to spare myself this humiliation, but . . . God never seems to take us when we want to go. My life is over. I know that. I'll never feel myself the same human being again. How will I face Treva? And Clint? And their children? How can I tell poor Grace when she comes home in a few more days? How can I walk down the aisle at church and not feel that every eye there is staring at my disgrace? My God, every soul in town will find out before we're ever cured. I've already had to tell Rose." (Rose Bliss was a schoolteacher Mother rented a room to after I left home the previous September.)

"But why, Mother? Was there any reason she had to know?"

"Of course. She was living here when we first found out what was wrong. If she had caught the disease from us in any remote way, she could have sued us. I *had* to tell her. But she is a good friend. I think I can trust her to keep it to herself. I'm very grateful to her. She's been good company for me now that my children are gone. She said she wasn't afraid of getting the disease. She's coming back next September. I'm glad. Needless to say, we need her rent."

When Father returned for supper, he looked at me and realized I had been told. He appeared very meek, and there was a begging in his eyes for forgiveness. But I had never before been put in the position of having to forgive my elders. I did not know what to say. It was a relief when Grace came home a few days later, to share with me the shock and disillusionment I felt. Grace had rejected marriage. She had a teaching job now in a small college in Nebraska. She had planned a summer trip to New York and New England with two other teachers from her school, but she felt that she should stay with us during the summer, that she might be needed if only to help try to console Mother. But Mother insisted she hold to her plans. "There's no point of your wasting a summer here at home, sitting on the front porch, listening to my troubles. Go. For God's sake, get away."

The only consolation to us all that summer, the first of the Depression, was that everyone was sad, and bewildered, and poor. The little town we lived in had lost the prop that had supported all its pride and confidence: wealth. Most of the beautiful, big homes were empty. One of the town's two leading banks had failed. Some of our close neighbors were destitute. Farmers could not sell their produce; they came to town every Saturday in patched overalls, their wives in cheap cotton dresses, and returned to their farms in the evening with their pockets empty.

The streets of the town now were filled with vagrants, some on foot, some in dilapidated old cars that looked ready for a junkheap, all trying to make their way West. Our personal misery at home should have been relieved by the thought of all these people who, fighting for subsistence, had lost whatever concern they might ever have had for moral righteousness. Prudery exists only among the secure. The country's tight puritan conscience was beginning to show the first signs of loosening. It was no longer a climate that was horrified by moral misdemeanors. Yet my parents suffered a personal despair that relegated the Depression to a background or setting.

Undoubtedly, many people inadvertently discovered the circumstance that my parents felt was "a curse" upon them, but there was no perceptible change in their friends' attitudes toward them. The neighbors were as convivial as ever, Mother's friends from the D.A.R. and the Ladies Guild still called, and the grocers and sales-people were still friendly. But Mother could not help but judge herself with cruel misgiving and feel that she was the object of scorn when she walked down the street; and my father continued to bear a silent guilt that weighed upon his shoulders, crumpling his stature, slowing his walk, making a pause in his speech (for the first time in his life, he developed an occasional stammer), like a man rejected by his God.

What most humiliated Mother was perhaps not the in-fliction of the disease itself, but the fact that it revealed to us children her still passionate desire for my father when both were in their sixties. Physical desire was some-thing she had never admitted to. "Women are not at-tracted to men in that way," she used to tell all of her children. "Why, your father and I haven't done anything silly like that for years." We all had believed her, gullibly. She told many times the story of her running away from Father after the first night of their marriage, because the sexual act was so frightening to her. She considered her fear a virtue. She was proud of it. But obviously, in coming back to him, her physical fright had gradually disappeared and she had discovered, after that first night of bleeding pain, the ecstasy that he could inject into her body and her senses, even though she claimed she did not love him.

I had never been able to imagine my mother and father in the act of sexual intercourse. After I first learned about copulation — from a precocious boy who sat across the aisle from me in the sixth grade and who told me about it one evening after school, in a way that made the act of love sound prurient and degrading — it was a long time before I could accept the fact that such an act, between my father and mother, could ever have taken place or brought me into the world.

"I don't know what made us act so silly that night," Mother confided to me later in the summer. "It was disgraceful of us at our age."

Father had never been able to talk to any of his children about personal matters. At first, he would not admit to Mother that he had had intercourse with another woman. He insisted that he had got the disease from a drinking cup, but he was unable to tell the story with conviction. Then, at one time, his temper flared, and he accused Mother of being the offender and giving the disease to *him*.

"How do *I* know who you see while I'm gone? You were familiar once with Doc Oates. How do I know . . ."

But Mother spat at him like a bobcat.

"Never! Never! Dr. Oates never laid a finger on me that way. Never! And if you ever accuse me of such a filthy thing again, I swear I'll kill you."

When Mother had confidence of her ground, she could be fierce. Dr. Oates had been dead now for several years, and so Father could not lay the blame on him.

"You can ask any of our neighbors, or Rose Bliss, or the children, if they've ever seen *any* man coming here to visit me. You're vile, Brian Hansen. You're a vile man for making such a cowardly accusation."

Finally, of course, Father admitted to her and to their doctor how he had contracted the disease. He shook with sobbing tears, like a confessing slayer, when he told the story. He had met one of his old friends one night, another traveling man, in the town of Junction City, which is close to an army base and so frequented by prostitutes. Father and his friend were staying at the same hotel. After dinner that night, they took a walk together, talking about business conditions and the effects of the Depression, and then went to one of their rooms and shared a few drinks of bootleg whiskey. As I said before, my father drank very seldom. When he did, the drink aroused desire. A porter at the hotel had told them he could provide them with a woman, and after the drinks, they both felt lusty. They called the porter and told him to send the woman to them. She came and gratified them both. Ironically, Father's friend, a man known as a "sport" who always enjoyed women in his bed when he was on the road, was not infected by the experience.

Mother had long had suspicions that my father enjoyed women when he was away, but it hurt her to have to face the fact that he actually had done so. He had wounded her just as if he had stabbed her in the flesh, and the wound would take years to heal and leave a lifelong scar. Her only solace was her conviction of moral justification over him, and her assurance of martyred innocence. Father was now a villain she could justifiably hate.

10.

MOST OF THE SUMMER, Mother and I were in the house alone. We would waken with the sun and come to the front porch and sit with the morning newspaper, just staring at the headlines, unable to respond to much of the news about the Depression. Early morning was the only time of the day when the air felt fresh, and we dreaded the day before us, the intense heat of noon, the loneliness of evening. We didn't have a car through the week in which to enjoy a drive.

Every morning on the front porch we would see Mrs. Holt leave her house and start for the Catholic church, on her way to mass. "She doesn't miss a day," Mother observed. There was a dedication about the woman that always gave us pause. "I wish *I* had a God to pray to now," Mother sometimes said, "but I don't seem able to find Him." Mother had stopped going to church. "Church isn't the place to go with your troubles. Church is just a place to go when you're feeling good and have a new hat to wear." There was a little bitterness in what she said, a little self-pity, but there was also truth. Our minister would have been the last person in the world she could have talked to, to have lifted the curse she felt upon her and saved her from feeling damned. She would have embarrassed the man into speechlessness had she gone to him with her story. He would have been unable to look at her or my father without coloring. Most of our morality, I was beginning to think, was based on a refusal to recognize sin. Our entire religious heritage, it seemed to me, was one of refusal to deal with it.

"I wonder how she'd feel if she were in my shoes," Mother sometimes said, watching Mrs. Holt on her way to mass. "Maybe other people suffer their misfortunes, too, and we never hear about them; but I feel now like the only person in the world God ignores."

She would try to refresh herself on those steaming hot days with memories of the summer in Colorado. "We were all together then. That was the last time I was ever with my entire family. That was a *happy* summer. I still remember how cool the days were, and how clear and sunny the mornings, and those beautiful drives Jule would take me on, through the mountains, at evening, when the sun was setting. Now, it's as if that happiness didn't mean anything. I guess it didn't, but I'd like to think it did. I'd like to think it meant I had some chance for future happiness, too. Happiness is just a phase we go through from time to time, like a season of pretty weather; and one lovely day is no promise at all that we'll ever see another."

On Friday evenings, Father would come driving back into the driveway, the car covered with dust, the back seat loaded with packing cases. By this time, he had given up the sample room and office he used to keep downtown in one of the hotels, and had converted a corner of our old barn to a room where he could pack his cases and do his desk work. I would always help him unload the car and put the back seat in, and then take Mother for a ride.

"Thank God for the car. If you've got a car, it at least means you don't have to sit at home with your worries and just watch the day pass. It at least means you can move and go someplace else, and get a change of scenery."

And on Saturday mornings, Mother and Father would get into the car again and go to the doctor's office, and return an hour later, Mother holding her arm where the needle had punctured her vein, as tenderly as she would hold a baby. Her eyes would be stung with hurt, and Father would be faceless with guilt; and they would be silent for a while with the pain they had suffered together. But eventually, Mother would find new justification for reviling him, like a fox tearing the flesh of a wounded buck. My father, for a while, would try to defend himself, and they would curse each other like prisoners sharing a room in Hell. There were times when I could not bear any longer to listen to their raving accusations, their senseless damning of each other that continued long after each had damned himself; I would have to hide down in the cellar, as Mother had taught us earlier to hide from storms.

Finally, Father ceased to defend himself, and sat speechless through her attacks. Then I would have to leave the house. I could not stay and watch his mute suffering.

I was able to keep one part of me immune to the hopelessness that filled our home, that filled the world that summer. I had begun to write more poems. Serious poems, and a little fiction. Maybe the poems grew out of my feeling of hopelessness that summer, for if we can mold our grief into some shapeful form, we have objectified it and put it into a shape that we can hold. Not all my poems, though, were melancholy or despairing. Sometimes a writer can create his happiest work in the midst of gloom. A few of the poems found print in the local newspaper, which gave me some satisfaction; and some were published by the Kansas City newspaper. But I had no success with the national publications, although I got encouraging letters from the editors of some magazines about some of the more serious poems I had submitted. I was beginning to strengthen with the confidence that a writing career was possible for me.

Also, there was Nell Ramsey, a girl I had been fond of since childhood, a beautiful girl with a quiet humor and a deep compassion for people. Her family was poor, too. They were Southern people who had been brought to Freedom in its prosperous days when the father was able to make a good living as an insurance broker. The Depression had destroyed his income and taken away his savings, and his Southern gentility had not equipped him to face a world become desperate with hunger pangs. The Ramseys existed meagerly during the Depression, dependent upon the bit of financial help Nell's older brother was able to give them from his earnings in a new aircraft plant in Wichita. At night, after supper, I would walk across the town to her house and sit on the front porch with Nell, sometimes her mother keeping us company (Nell's father was much older than his wife and always retired early, exhausted by the day, not caring to prolong it). Mrs. Ramsey was a fleshy, good-natured woman, who must really have come from a long line of Southern aristocrats because she was the only Southerner I had ever known who didn't brag nostalgically about the vanished splendor of her youth, and talk about Negroes as if they were house pets. She showed in her ability to face a world that had begun to change very rapidly, a sadness that proved she realized what the changes meant, and a courage which is the greatest attribute of breeding, without which all the other attributes of social grace and charm are meaningless and silly. Mrs. Ramsey still could be jolly, despite the fact that life had disillusioned her like a bad movie, overpraised in its advertisements.

If I had the money, I would take Nell to a movie, in her father's old Hudson if I didn't have access to my father's old Dodge. If I didn't have the money, she would take me or we would "go dutch." We had to scheme to provide ourselves with cigarettes. We even took for a while to rolling our own, from a sack of Bull Durham, on a little rolling machine that had just been put on the market that usually produced cigarettes shaped like a telescope, stringy at the ends. But they were better than those we tried to roll by hand, so wet with saliva we couldn't light them.

And despite the unspoken gloom that pervaded my home, and despite the misery of the world, there were summer evenings as sweet in my memory as lavender. Evenings in the nearby hills, on wiener roasts with friends Nell and I had grown up with in town, once in a while having the money to chip in on "spiked" beer for stimulation, or a bottle of bootleg whiskey or gin. And there were casual evenings at the country club that had opened its door to all the young people in town who could afford a small fee to spend the evening dancing to a jukebox and using the swimming pool and picnic grounds. Nights when the bright orange moon and the crystal stars hung in the sky like the only promises that had been kept for the world. And there was always the heartening, bracing rhythm of jazz, and the consolation of popular songs. "Stardust," "If I Could Be with You," "I Want a Little Girl" could be heard on any jukebox. They were as much a part of the summer as the heat, the fear and the hunger.

There might have been romance that summer, too, but after my one ugly experience at college, I was still frightened of physical love. This fear of course was reinforced by the predicament I had found my parents in upon returning home. I was as frightened in Nell Ramsey's arms as I had been years before of swimming in the sea, and unable to think of the sexual act as anything but a degrading thrill that could only cheapen a girl I had respect for. Perhaps Nell was as shy as I was, for our physical relations were as cautious as one's treatment of invalids. A kiss goodnight, a warm embrace, a holding of hands were the only intimate contacts we attempted.

But there was the sensual enjoyment of Ned Brooks's company, who was working as lifeguard at the city swimming pool out in Riverside Park during the summer. Ned was two years older than I, which meant that during high school, when I was a sophomore and he a senior, he seemed of another generation, wiser and more sophisticated than mine. But he and his mother lived only a block or two from us, so occasionally Ned and I would walk home from school together in the afternoons. I felt flattered then to be in the company of the most luminous senior in the high school, a star football player, an A student, a handsome fellow that all the girls in school wanted for a boyfriend, and a good-natured fellow that any boy would want for a friend. Now the two years' difference didn't matter in our ages, and we became fast friends.

Ned Brooks had just ended his junior year at Washburn College in Topeka, where he had won a football scholarship and planned to enter the law school. But times were so hard for him and his widowed mother, he didn't know how he'd manage to return to school in September. The job at the pool payed very little. His mother did sewing and baked bread and sold a line of knit dresses to help run the house. During the school year, she took in boarders, most of them schoolteachers. It was whispered during our high school years that Ned was having a love affair with the pretty young Spanish teacher who had just joined the faculty my sophomore year.

When I would go out to the pool in the morning, during this particular summer, and lie with Ned on the lifesaver's high derrick, we would have long, intimate talks.

"Of course I fucked her, Joey. Whatta ya *think* I was doing, driving her Packard around all the time, visiting her apartment at night? Ya think she was giving me Spanish lessons? You don't believe that people really fuck, *do* ya, Joey?" he laughed.

It was true, I didn't. I had learned all my morals from the movies and supposed unquestioningly that girls in real life could be just as provocative and inviting as Clara Bow and still be innocent of sexual intention. The teacher was Carmel Draper, and unlike most schoolteachers, she was wealthy, or of wealthy parents. She was teaching only to pass the time while she was waiting for her fiancé to finish his internship in an Eastern hospital, when they would get married. "She just didn't wanna wait to have her fun," Ned explained. "I was more than willing to oblige. Man! I don't know what kind of teacher she was in the classroom, but she sure educated *me.*"

I felt very attracted to one who took his physical prowess so easily for granted, and functioned sexually as casually as he breathed or ate his food and eliminated it. He had had a reputation for sexual daring ever since his days as a Boy Scout when he had seduced a girl in the river when some of the young people went swimming at a big church picnic, no one knowing but a few of his buddies, who had helped to shield the couple from the view of the church elders. It was known also that Ned had seduced, or been seduced *by*, the very pretty young starlet of a repertory show that had played a week's engagement one summer in the late Twenties, out on our fairgrounds in a tent they carried with them from town to town. Ned had been hired with a crew of other high school boys to perform the manual labor for the acting company, putting up the tent and taking it down, working backstage moving scenery during the week, and as ushers. The young starlet, who a few years later became a picture star, had first won regional fame in a Charleston contest held in Dallas. Her ambitious mother then had financed the road show, exploiting her daughter as star. The girl acted in some of the plays and did specialty numbers, singing and dancing, between the acts. Ned was seventeen when this brief romance happened to him; the girl, twenty, but in publicity releases, sixteen. Ned's sexual success with the girl, discovered by the other boys on the crew, gave him a prestige among his contemporaries comparable to that of a champion prizefighter. Ned finally verified this story for me, too. It sounded, as he told it, much like Fanny Hill's encounter with the handsome boy who brings her a letter from her master.

Ned was not one to brag about these experiences. It was my own curiosity that dragged them out of him, as if I wanted to live them vicariously. It seemed miraculous to me that one could be so lighthearted about sex when it had created such a conflagration in my own home. It never occurred to Ned that he had done anything "wicked" or "obscene." And he retained a wholesomeness of character that separated him from the boys at the pool hall who practiced sex as a vice. Every Sunday morning, Ned Brooks put on his blue serge suit and took his mother to church, and other mothers admired him when he walked with her down the aisle and sat beside her. He felt no hypocrisy at all in going to church and having sexual pleasure, too.

I told him about my one sexual experience at the university, and he laughed. "Joey, you shouldn't waste your time on sluts. Sex isn't any fun unless you *feel* something for the girl. You got yourself in the wrong hole. That's all."

One evening Ned drove by in the Model T Ford he had brought home from college, painted with crazy signs and cartoons. He came up on our porch and spoke charmingly to Mother ("My, he's a handsome young man. I bet he's a good driver, too. I can always tell a good driver.") and suggested I go with him to a movie. I had already asked Nell to go with me, so I suggested we all go together. "Nell Ramsey?" Ned asked. "I haven't seen her in a long time." Because of the difference in their ages, Ned had not taken serious notice of Nell in high school, and had forgotten her entirely during college. I think I probably knew, when we went to her door that night and she came out smiling, wearing a fresh white cotton dress, that she and Ned would fall in love. When we went to the Candy Kitchen after the movie and ordered Cokes, the same Candy Kitchen where Treva had said goodbye to Frank Bradshaw, they could not take their eyes off each other. I sat beside Nell in the booth, but I might as well not have been there.

"Joey, maybe it'd be easier if I took you home first," Ned said when we went to his car. " 'Cause Nell's house is closer to mine."

"Sure, Ned," I replied good-naturedly, and Nell said nothing.

I returned to our dark house and answered Mother when she called from her bed to ask if it was me. I kissed her on the cheek, goodnight, and went to my room. Then a feeling of desolation came over me. The two people who had been closer to me and more beloved than any I had ever known outside of my family, now belonged to each other. My friendship with either of them would never possess the same exclusiveness. And yet it was I who had given them to each other, as though something inside me had wanted to be free of them both. I lay awake the rest of that night. I may have cried. And I know I felt frightened by my compulsion to be excluded from any personal relationship that threatened to be binding.

II.

IN AUGUST, when the sun had baked the grass to straw, and the heat had become so fierce that people stayed inside their darkened homes all through the long afternoons, with wet towels hung up before their electric fans, until finally, at sundown, the sun's intensity would lessen, and people felt safe to venture back to their porches or try to resurrect life in their lawns with garden hoses; in this white hell of August heat, Father became stricken with a rash of raw sores that broke out on his body like a plague. The rash created an insane itching. He could not wear any clothes next to him. Dr. Damon was called. He examined Father and sent him to the hospital. He first pronounced it to be poison ivy or oak, but later admitted it was an allergic reaction to the shots that he had been giving my father for about five months. Father remained in the hospital for two weeks.

Now I felt it my duty to visit my father every afternoon. A duty, but one I did not resent. I wanted to visit him because for the first time in my life, I felt some pity for this man who I had always been told was my father, but who had seemed no more related to me than a school principal or a boss. Only my senses told me the suffering he was undergoing, for he was a typical Western man and never admitted to it. He accepted his suffering as an animal does, without complaining, without blaming it on anyone, but just enduring it because he knew there was nothing else for him to do; but his agony filled his eyes with dread. He looked like some tortured creature in a Grünewald painting, lying on his back, his entire body erupted in poisonous sores that the nuns at the hospital kept covered with a milky solution that dried on his flesh and helped it to heal. Lying thus on his back for two weeks, having to resist every desire to scratch his tantalizing flesh, in the breathless heat of August, it was as if my own manhood lay beside him and suffered his wounds. Every time I visited him, I felt closer to him, even though we knew each other so little we never found anything to talk about except the weather, the Depression news, maybe a card from Grace or a letter from Treva. But the world and its affairs were remote to him now. All he could think of was the cessation of his torment. Still, his salesman's spirit would rally to find something a little humorous to remark upon, and he would always insist that he was "a little better today, son. Yes, I think I'm a little better."

What could I do to help this man who was my father? What could I do to lessen his pain? A man who had never read a book in the years I had known him, who would find no joy in flowers, or cards, or games. I could not think of a time when I had seen him enjoy himself, not even at the baseball games he once in a while took me to when I was younger, or at the one movie he had taken me to when I was a boy, or at the big Halloween festivals our little town always celebrated with parades and dances and vaudeville programs. My father had always behaved as if any pleasurable experience was to be distrusted, and he could never give himself wholly to it.

I remembered him once enjoying himself at a big family reunion one of his sisters had held on her family's farm down in Oklahoma; there, my father saw all of his aunts and uncles and cousins and their children, and his own father who was close to ninety and had made the trip, with a younger brother, from Oklahoma City where he had gone to live after Grandmother died. With his own kin, my father seemed a different man, at ease, gentle, full of friendly talk. I remembered, too, seeing a delight in his eyes when he saw a great field of golden wheat ready for harvest, and when he took me through Uncle Maynard's barn and showed me the livestock. What a very simple man he was. How very little he had ever expected from life. How false he made me feel when he smiled gently and refused the expensive Havana cigars I once brought to the hospital. Tobacco was the only diversion that he had now. "I like the cheap ones, son. The costly cigars are wasted on me. I never developed a taste for expensive things."

✓ Was there really an Old Testament God who punished us as my father was now being punished for his *sins?* If there was, I thought I must hate Him. For now I loved my father. For the first time in my life, I saw inside his frightened heart and forgave him all my childhood resentments: he had never made himself a part of my life, or shown me how to live as a boy, or shared anything personal with me that would acknowledge me as his son. He had not even given me a present. Never had he brought me a knife, or a pair of skates, or a bicycle. Even at Christmas, the presents had all been selected by Mother, given us with a card in her writing: "From Mom and Dad." When we opened them on Christmas morning, Father didn't even know what the presents were until we showed them to him, and thanked him dutifully. Never had I known one spontaneous act of generosity or love from him. Yet, he was concerned if I was ever ill; and he had seen to it that I had my chance to go to college, even though the money to send me there came hard to him, and he had little to spare. Why had he felt it so important for me to go to college? Why had he shown this one serious concern?

One day, visiting him in the darkened hospital room, the shades all drawn to keep out the hellish sun, just the sound of an electric fan and the nuns' vigilant steps on the concrete floors, I knew: he had felt an intuitive worry about my future, and was trusting others to prepare me for life, knowing he had failed. And he had never been generous with me because he never felt he had anything of himself or his possessions that was worth giving. It was not true, after all, that he did not love me. He just had never had the confidence to give. And love is a gift, the hardest gift of all to part with.

"My dear Father," I would have liked to say, "please forgive me for not understanding you all these years. I see now how hard your life has been. I see the fear with which you meet it. I understand the fear. I forgive you anything. And I love you."

I would have liked to say these things. But he wouldn't have understood them. He had grown up in a world which didn't permit a man expression of feeling. All I could do was to bring him cheap cigars.

And when I left the hospital and got into the old Dodge to drive home, I realized, after finding my love for my father, that I bore a hatred for my mother. It was *she* who had robbed him of his courage to live, it was *she* who had made him feel unworthy, who had hated his manhood from the first day of their marriage, and yet had wanted the pleasure of it, too. I prayed: *Oh dear Christ, don't let me hate her as I feel I must. She is my mother. And I have loved her desperately. Don't let me look into the evil she has done or I'll never be able to believe in anything sacred again. Spare me, please, from the vision of two people I want to love, whom I must love in order to live, whose decency is sham, whose virtue is pretense, who have masked themselves before their own children and hidden the truth of their lives as if it was a fury that would destroy us.*

Once again, I swung the car into the familiar curve of the driveway, and got out to walk up the front steps and enter the house and face my mother, this time as a frightening stranger, but whom, before this time, I had always longed to see.

12.

THE YEAR AT HOME attending the small junior college was like a period in purgatory. School days lacked
the excitement that they had had at the university, though
there was a pleasure in being again with some of my high
school friends. Both Nell and Ned were students with me.
There were no classes for Ned in the junior college that
would advance his degree in law, but he used his time to
take language and literature courses he had not had time
to take previously. And he had found a part-time job in
the afternoons delivering groceries for one of the big
markets in town. He and Nell were together constantly.
Sometimes the three of us would take in a movie together,
or I would get a date with another girl and we would go to
a dance, or play cards. And I became a good friend of Rose
Bliss, the teacher who roomed with us. She was a hearty,
good-natured woman who helped to relieve the sense of
grief that burdened our house, as much from my mother's
and father's muted hostility when he was home over the

weekends as from my mother's quiet brooding when he was gone. Sometimes of an evening Rose would make a pot of fudge with nutmeats, and we would talk or play cards, sitting before the fire while Mother knitted or sewed. And I began to read more: Mann, Proust, Lawrence, Fitzgerald, Kafka, Dostoevski, Tolstoy. The year passed, and another summer. The year was marked by only one unexpected incident, the sudden death of my Uncle Jay, which took Mother and me back to Wichita a few days where, again, we stayed with Aunt Patsy.

When I returned to the university the next autumn, I was, for the times, an affluent young man. Uncle Jay had left me five thousand dollars when he died. This was a glad surprise. He left the same to Grace and Treva. Also, Professor Havemeyer of the English Department at the university had arranged for me to have a scholarship. I was moved that he valued my ability enough to do this. Both gifts came from men with whom I had had very little contact, who I supposed had little awareness of my existence. I was able now to buy a couple of good suits and allow myself more than one pair of shoes, and indulge a taste for broadcloth and madras shirts and lisle hosiery and colorful neckties. I also bought a camel's hair coat and some good luggage. I returned to the fraternity, sorry to discover that Bob Luther had not returned but had transferred to a school of mines in Colorado.

(I was to see him once again, when we met by chance at the New York World's Fair just before the Second World War.

He introduced me to his wife, a young woman who wore too much makeup and spoke in an unpleasant nasal voice, expressing only platitudinous sentiments in her conversation. If I had seen her alone, I'd have taken her for a prostitute. I could tell that Bob was embarrassed by her. Why had he married a woman so beneath him, I wondered. Was it because of some lack of faith in himself?

He was now a mining engineer, just turned thirty, living in Denver. We sat at one of the outdoor cafés and tried to make conversation, but it was difficult. I was quietly shocked to find that he was a heated isolationist, opposed to the United States coming to the aid of Britain; if anything, he thought that we should be on the side of the Nazis helping to rid the world of Jews. I had never seen Bob's potential for such fanaticism in the fraternity. What threats had he felt in meeting the world after college that had created in him such angry prejudices? What pressures had driven him to seek comfort in such vicious, irrational defensiveness? What private fears had converted a potentially heroic young man, as I had always thought him, into this soulless, unthinking shell? I crossed him out of my memories as one crosses out the name of a dead friend from an address book.)

Upon return to the university, I should have enrolled as a junior, but I had declined to fill all my freshman-sophomore requirements at the junior college at home because doing so would have forced me to take a course in math. At the university, with its vaster curriculum, I could substitute an ancient language for math, and so I deliberately waited until I returned there to finish these requirements. I would have taken any other course to avoid the exactitude of mathematics. I enrolled in Beginning Greek. I could not fully declare myself an English major until I finished my required courses, so I regarded all other courses as so many hurdles I had to top before I could devote myself totally to writing and the study of literature.

Again I found Betsy Parsons, and in the same scholastic predicament I was in, taking Greek to avoid math. Again, she sat beside me in class. Betsy was now a celebrity on the campus, having given admirable performances in many college drama productions. She was a bright girl, but her studies bored her. The one serious interest in her life was the theater; but her interest in boys and in having a good time was serious, too. She never studied. She passed Greek by cribbing off my exams, which I was always happy to let her see. During recitations, I often prompted her under my breath so that the teacher, a kindly old lady who couldn't have believed that any of us cheated, could not hear. How favored I felt to sit beside Betsy! What an honor it was for me to let her crib off my exam! I can always remember her hurrying to class in the morning, usually a few minutes late, for which she'd smile ingratiatingly at Miss

Deacon, our professor, who'd say then, "You really must be a little more prompt, Miss Parsons."

"Oh, Miss Deacon, I'm *so* sorry, but I honestly couldn't help it this time," and Miss Deacon would smile and forgive her and start the recitation. Then the worldly aroma of her perfume would fill my senses as she took her seat and straightened her dress and fussed with her pencils and note paper, making sure that the chic little hat she was wearing had not got twisted to some unflattering angle in all her rush, and arranging the fur collar on her coat so that it would not rub against the back of the chair. The class met three mornings a week at eight o'clock. I looked forward to each meeting. Upon her frequent absences, my heart sank when I realized that Betsy was not being late again but was not coming to class, and the rest of the day I would feel deprived. But how happy I'd be to see her again after she'd recovered from the virus ("Oh, Joey, I had the most awful attack of flu. I couldn't get out of bed for days. You must be careful of it, Joey. There's so much of it going around now, and it's some kind of new virus they say is really deadly.") and would take her seat next to me again and I'd feel the sweet scented warmth of her person close and dear.

I honestly did not realize I was in love with her. I did not know I was allowed to be. She was everything that the movies, the magazines, the funny papers had taught me was most adorable in a girl; and I felt myself much too insignificant in her world even to dream about her.

[174]

After Beginning Greek, I saw less of her. Only acciden-
tally would we pass on campus, to and from classes. She
was usually hanging onto the gladiatorial arm of one of
the athletes, who towered over her, she having to look up
into his stern face as she chatted with him, pedaling her tiny
feet to take two steps to his one. This, of course, was the
kind of man whom I visualized for her mate. The two of
them together had no relation at all with the sweaty, eye-
strained world of my own, which studies and writing filled
almost completely, with only a few pleasures squeezed in,
like seeing the movies on weekends or stealing time to read
a new Somerset Maugham novel, or resuming my trips into
Kansas City to see a show or hear a concert. She would
always greet me with a "Hello, Joey-pie!" (her own nick-
name for me, a contraction of Joey and Sweetie-pie, her
favorite term of casual endearment), and I would feel
blessed, and my heart would again glow for a while, until
long sessions at the library and tense conferences with my
adviser, Professor Kitchell, slowly brought me back into the
world that was my own.

The next year, after I'd worked hard enough to get classified as a senior, I was asked by the head of the Drama
Department, upon Professor Havemeyer's recommenda-
tion, to help with the translation of *Antigone* that he was
preparing for Betsy to star in. This work brought me close
to her again, for I had to attend rehearsals with the direc-
tor and work on the dialogue when it didn't function right
for the actors. And I liked going to rehearsals just to watch

Betsy work. Only then did I see the serious side of her other-wise frivolous character. Later, I played small parts in some of the plays just to be with her. She played Eliza in *Pygmalion*, and the leading female roles in *Peter Pan* and *They Knew What They Wanted*. I saw everything she did and adored her. She was admitted everywhere on campus to be "an unusually talented girl," even by the most sophisti-cated people on the faculty. It was assumed that of course she would have a career in the theater.

But there are two strong forces working against each other in every creative person. During her years of col-lege, Betsy continued working in the theater, growing all that time as an actress; but offstage, she was beginning to estrange herself from the elite social life on the campus. Even in my junior year, I had heard talk about her from some of my fraternity brothers. One of them, Skip Hollo-way, who had dated her the previous year when I was at-tending the junior college at home, told the other men in the house impressive stories of her sexual passion. I paid no more attention to the stories than I paid to all the imaginative rumors one heard at the time about the per-sonal lives of Garbo and Tallulah Bankhead and Dietrich. It seemed only right that such a glamorous woman should be gossiped about. I kept silent when I heard my brothers talking about Betsy. Their talk only belittled them, I thought; but in her junior year, Betsy got expelled from her sorority, and the explanation that spread around cam-pus was that she had been discovered in the sexual act with a young man whose name was never divulged, so little importance did his involvement make in the story, late one night in the sorority kitchen. But her glory still was not dimmed for me.

There is a willful independence in some creative people that dares them to defy the laws of man, the laws of God Himself, with blind valor. The ordinary sorority girl, caught in such a circumstance, would have dropped out of school immediately (at that particular time in our social and moral history) and returned home to live in embarrassment, perhaps for the rest of her life. Betsy only moved out of her sorority, explaining that the girls there were really "too simpleminded" for her, anyway, and moved into a tiny apartment "where for God's sake I can do as I damn please without having to worry about a lot of snoopy, evil-minded little bitches trying to make me lead the same stupid lives that they lead." I was proud of her. Bernhardt or Duse would have done the same thing. I myself accepted the conformity of a fraternity because, at the time I had no very conscious need for a way of life different from that that the other men in the house subscribed to; but I could see the situation of the artist and society much more clearly in the case of Betsy and her sorority. I stood up for Betsy wholeheartedly and hated my fraternity brothers for their new scorn of her. Now that she had devalued herself sexually in their eyes, they could not appreciate her in any aspect, though she was still as beautiful, as charming and as talented as she had ever been. They could not openly date her or be seen with her at any school function. To do so would have been to lose caste. The homely boys in the fraternity, those whom Betsy never would have looked at twice as possible lovers, were the most scornful of her now. It fulfilled them to bring down, in their conversation, an image that had always enticed them but which they could never have possessed. The male ego, I began to realize, could be very vengeful.

The only friends left to Betsy were the bohemians on campus, the miscellaneous group of students who had happened onto the campus from all parts of the United States, who gathered together in each other's basements or attics to read Baudelaire, or talk about Marx or Dostoevski or Joyce or Proust, to denounce conservative government, and deride conventional art and literature. Betsy's scandal had not concerned them. Some of them were so removed from sorority-fraternity life, they had not even heard the story of her expulsion from the sorority. As an English major who was just beginning to come intellectually alive at this time, I lived with some awareness of the bohemians in school, and was occasionally tolerated at their parties even though I belonged to a fraternity. This they forgave me. I never revealed these adventures with the bohemians to my fraternity brothers, fearing I'd be looked upon as a traitor to their way of life, but I was slowly beginning to find more pleasure and certainly more stimulation among them than I did among my "brothers." These people accepted Betsy with the serene generosity of the Salvation Army.

There were no racial barriers among the bohemians, or the "Barbs." Among them, I was able for the first time to meet with Negroes as social equals. The Negro student most prized in their company was Ron Fuller, one of the greatest athletes who had ever come to the campus, and an honor student. He made All-American two years in a row on the football team, and starred spectacularly in several track events. He was handsome, well-mannered, serenely male in his manner, and so clean in his dress and person that he often appeared out of place in the company of some of the white bohemians, who could not differentiate between grooming and social conformity. Ron was seen frequently in the company of white girls, but none with the distinction of Betsy. The first time they met, at a Saturday night spaghetti dinner in the basement apartment of Rosita Palomar and her friend Josephine Tetsly, where lots of red wine was served with the dinner, and the candles burned to pools of hot wax by the time the people left, Betsy and Ron were immediately attracted to each other. He took her home from the party, to her tiny apartment and undoubtedly spent the night with her. Thereafter, they were seen everywhere together on the campus and in the town. The rest of the university was stunned by the sight of the two together. The men students were angered by Ron's sexual trespassing, even though with a girl they had presumably ostracized from their society. They hated Betsy now for the fact that their scorn had not diminished her appeal, and for the look of arrogance on her face when she walked down the campus with Ron; and they hated Ron for refusing to look ashamed and guilty, for acting as nonchalant as if there were no reason in the world for his not being with Betsy. Ron had always been cheered by the student body as a hero, and students loved to brag about what a fine man he was, "even though he is a Negro," and "of course he's better than many whites"; and he had even been invited to some of the fraternity houses for dinner and treated proudly. Now, the resentment of him was so bitter, school authorities became fearful of his physical safety. The Dean of Men called Ron into his private office for a long conference. The Dean of Women called Betsy into her private office for a long conference. Both students resented the interference in their private lives so bitterly that they clung to each other more possessively than ever, and dared society ever more tauntingly to destroy their love affair. Betsy was forced to move again, being evicted from the tiny apartment for sheltering Ron. When the landlord came to give her notice, he called her a *whore* and she spat in his face. Something in her enjoyed the social challenge she was accepting, and rendered her invulnerable to whatever personal hurt she might feel from the wounds she was getting. Of the two, Ron was much more realistic. He had never wanted to exploit their romance. He wouldn't permit her to kiss him publicly even at the intimate parties among the bohemians. But Betsy could not resist a general advertising of their affair, making it look at times as though she did not love Ron as much as she wanted to shock the little world around her she so hated. It was not until she became pregnant by him that she was trapped into facing with full honesty some of the consequences of her behavior.

"Joey," she said to me, in a faint, sad little voice that was expressing her own emotion now and not some playwright's, "I wish to God I could die." The abortion was over by this time, and I was visiting her in the room she rented from a widowed landlady who did not keep moral supervision over her roomers. For once, Betsy had handled a crisis in her life without advertising it to the entire campus. The fact of her pregnancy was known only to Ron and me and Rosita and Josephine. The romance between her and Ron ended automatically with her trip to the doctor. He could not bring himself even to come see her, and like two criminals, both felt fearful of being seen together now, as if their names might be linked in connection with the crime they had committed: they had disposed of a life. "I feel so empty," Betsy cried. "Think what a wonderful child we could have had together. Oh, I hate myself for giving it up. I feel like such a bitch. I hate myself, Joey. I don't feel I can ever like myself again."

It all happened just a few weeks before the Spring Relays, an annual track competition that Ron was training for. Ron had to report for practice every afternoon, but the emotion he was experiencing plus the strenuous physical exertion of his workouts was taking a toll of his energy. He appeared to have lost weight, and his bright, coppery skin was darkened to a muddy color around the eyes. There was another anxiety in his life now: he was being considered for a Rhodes Scholarship, which he wanted so desperately to win he could hardly talk about it. Meeting me, he inquired after Betsy with genuine concern, but he was faced with the disturbing fact that he had never loved her, realizing now that the desire they had felt for each other was born out of a mutual hate for a world which they both felt was stupid and beneath them, which they wanted to shock and defy. Once their gesture of defiance had been made, they could only admit, each to himself, that the stupid world had not changed because of it, and only themselves had suffered. "Tell Betsy I hope for the best for her," Ron told me. I said I would. And he was relieved to know that the operation had not caused her any physical pain or damage. I had never known anyone so sensitive about pain as Ron. He lived in fear of inadvertently inflicting it upon the white people he cared for. I think he must have been so full of hatred for our race, he feared that that hatred might suddenly expose itself in some unconscious act of violence he could not account for.

"He used to hurt me at first," Betsy told me later, with a candor that was impressive, though not entirely plausible. Perhaps she wanted to make me jealous of the one grand operatic love in her life which she would never be able to forget. "He was so big there, you know. Oh, my God, I have never seen anything like it. It frightened me. It made me bleed at first. And the way he'd talk while we were doing it, some of the things he'd say were so exciting, like he was talking to a whore, but then he'd always be terribly sweet afterward to show me he didn't mean it. Do you mind if I tell you this, Joey?" Before I could reply, she went on, "He'd cover my whole body with soft kisses, his hot breath warming me in the most intimate little places until I felt such rapture I'd have to scream and bite him and scratch, and then he'd laugh at me like a giant at a pygmy. Oh, Joey, it was all crazy and pointless, but I did have the feeling of being loved by a god, a dark, angry god."

The abortion had been easily managed by one of the respected doctors in town, who, upon finding that Betsy's child had a Negro father, did not haggle about the ethical issue involved but performed the operation upon her immediately, with a housewife's impatience to clean up a mess on the floor before company arrives. "After it was over, he treated me as if I were just a tiny bit loathsome," Betsy confided to me, trying to take it all philosophically. The only pain was emotional, the feeling of emptiness she endured, her inability for a long time thereafter to take any interest in anything that happened around her. She quit going to classes and finished the semester with Incompletes in all her courses. She stayed in her room most of the time and almost never went out. Other students forgot her.

The afternoon of the Relays I spent with her. The town was full of cars from all over the state, many from other states, and it was a warm, sunny day in late April. We sat in the window seat of Betsy's room and watched the endless, crowded procession of cars down the street on their way to the stadium. The sidewalks were filled, too, with people walking to the games, carrying banners. All over town, one could hear the bumptious band music playing for the slowly filling stadium. The air was charged with excitement. Ron was one of the heroes of the day. He placed first in three major events, and the entire crowd cheered him, even the student body that a short time before had resented his sexual presumption. All that was forgotten in his triumph.

We could hear the cheering from Betsy's window. I had brought a program along so we could follow the events that were taking place. We could even hear some of the announcements over the loud speaker. The atmosphere outside blared with triumph. Betsy's loss was trivial and private. "Oh, Joey, what's going to happen to me?" she asked in a helpless little voice. Unconsciously, I put an arm around her in an effort to be consoling.

"You're very sweet, Joey," she said, taking the hand that rested on her shoulder and kissing it. "I don't know what I'd have done without you. I honestly don't. You don't think I'm terrible, do you, Joey-pie?"

"Of course not, Betsy," I could reply truthfully and without hesitation. I felt it a privilege to think I might have been of help to her. It had never occurred to me during any of Betsy's tribulation that she had cheapened or corrupted herself in any way. I had watched her life on campus as I would watch a great performance on stage, never criticizing Betsy for her behavior any more than I would have criticized Madame X or Sadie Thompson. Everything Betsy did, I converted in my own mind to drama.

"Kiss me, Joey," she said, and before I even had time to carry out her order, she placed a hand at the back of my head and brought my mouth to hers. "You're cute, Joey, Do you know it?" (If I was, I didn't.) "You've never realized a girl might want you to make love to her, have you?" (I never had. How did she know?) "You're sweet, Joey. That's what girls really like in a man, didn't you know it? They want a man who understands them and can be sweet. You understand me, Joey. And you're very sweet." She hugged me closer to her and for the first time I felt the reality of her flesh next to mine, and the fullness of her breasts against me. She giggled. "It's almost as if I were the boy making love to a shy girl." Then, for the first time, I dared to assert myself. Some unrecognized urge took over and commanded me, and without even knowing what was happening, I accepted my maleness. Betsy had given it to me, easily and without fuss, and it was the greatest gift that I had ever received. I dared to become a man that afternoon, and to love her with all the careful tenderness

[185]

that she had been unconsciously wanting all this time, with the tenderness I had been unconsciously wanting to give.

I broke my membership in my fraternity a week or so later when its officers refused to let me bring Betsy to our annual spring party. I took a room close to her and we were together constantly except when I was in class. We attended together a small party one of the assistant professors in the Drama Department gave for Ron, where most of our bohemian friends were present. Ron had been accepted as a Rhodes Scholar. It was the first time he and Betsy had met since her trip to the doctor. He had brought a Negro girl with him to the party. Both Ron and Betsy, when they met again, tried to act as though nothing serious had ever happened between them. We all gave him presents and wished him well. We never saw him again. At the end of that school year, Betsy went home to Carthage, Missouri, and I to my home in Freedom. We corresponded constantly. I had decided to stay in school until I finished my master's degree. Betsy had "definite plans" to go to New York and try to break into show business. We never discussed the possibility of marriage, both taking it for granted that it would be a hindrance as we began our careers. One day in July, I got a card from her saying "I'm off." A few weeks later, there was a letter from New York, full of hopes about getting a small "but good" part in a new Maxwell Anderson play. My feeling of loss, so painful at first, began slowly to diminish. The last letter I wrote to her was returned, marked ADDRESS UNKNOWN. Something now was missing from my life for which, again, I would have to find compensation in my work.

13.

I WORKED VERY HARD, going to summer school, finishing my B.A. and then my master's degree in less than three years. By this time, my inheritance was spent and I needed a job to support myself. I quickly got one at a small girls' college close to Kansas City. And then I panicked my first day of teaching. It was probably the realization that I was now facing life entirely on my own. At times, I longed for the nearness and sweetness of Betsy, but I had given up trying to get in touch with her. She seemed to have disappeared from the earth. For some reason, I did not feel prepared for life. Something in me still cried for a child's dependence. I was terrorized by the idea of my teaching classes. I felt inferior to my colleagues, most of whom had much more impressive degrees than mine, from Harvard and Yale and the University of Chicago. The first weekend of my new job, I took the train home, and told my parents I wanted to stay. They stared at me dumbly. They were getting old now, they deserved to be free from the dependence of their children.

"What will you do if you stay here, Joey?" Mother asked. "There's no sort of work for you in *this* town."

"Your mother and I have done all for you we can, son," my father advised me, baffled to understand the predicament I felt myself in. "If you don't make it in this job, I don't know *what* you'll do."

So I returned to my job, remembering during the train ride back the childhood game of hide-and-seek I used to play. Then, the child who was It, after counting to fifty while the other players found their hiding places, would cry out, *Ready or not, here I come*! And that was the attitude I had to take now, beginning my life in the world away from home.

Finally I came to relax a little in my work. And only then, paradoxically, I began to realize that I did not like teaching, that I was a misfit in the profession. Still, I had to earn a living. And with teaching there were the advantages of having enough time to do a little writing, and to travel, on a very small budget, during the summers. Now that I had made my break from home, I resisted going back. I spent my first summer's vacation in New York, the second in California. Mother's letters were full of hurt that I didn't return. So I cut short my stay in the mountains around Big Sur, where I was staying with one of my colleagues in a cabin he owned there, and took the train home to stay for two weeks before reporting back to my classes.

Summer was ending when I got there. The leaves had

begun to turn and the nights had become cool. There was a quiet in the atmosphere, a sense of waiting for the season to change, and a sadness in seeing summer go. Life wouldn't begin again until autumn appeared, with children going back to school, and football games, and the blooming of bittersweet and goldenrod on the surrounding hills.

It was two years now since I had been home. Mother and Father met my train and greeted me happily. For dinner that night, Mother had baked chocolate cake, and fried chicken — my favorite dinner when I was a small boy — and kept filling up my plate. I felt remiss that I could not respond as gladly upon my return as they, but I had lived apart from them long enough that our lives had little in common. To them, my life since leaving home was not real. We no longer had anything to share except memories of the past.

One evening I took Mother for a ride again, out to the park, and Riverside Drive, and Monkey Island. I almost could have forgotten that I had ever been away.

Mother was in her seventies now. "I never thought I'd live so long," she said. "When I was a girl, few people lived beyond the age of forty. I keep thinking I should feel differently to be as old as I am."

She was still very spry. She still did all of her own housework with an impatient frenzy to "keep things in order." And she couldn't resist shaming my father because "he does nothing but sit around the house all day. The only times he gets up out of his chair are to get the morning paper and come to his meals. There can't be anything serious wrong with him. He certainly hasn't lost his appetite."

My father was a destroyed man. As Mother said, he did very little around the house but sit in the big overstuffed chair we still kept beside the fireplace, and chew tobacco (how Mother always hated the slimy spittoon) when he wasn't smoking a cigar. He had not worked for a couple of years. "I don't know what's the matter with me, son. I don't seem to have any energy." And he looked much older than he actually was. Two years younger than Mother, he was very feeble and had to help himself up and down stairs with the banister. Mother seemed to flaunt her energy before him as if to shame him. But my father now was too passive, too indifferent to life to care.

The entire town was filled with buxom widows who had outlived their husbands by many years, who lived richly off the savings their husbands had destroyed themselves to earn. These men had lived the lives of drudges, and gone to early graves unmoved by passion, untouched by anything sublime. Their wives lived on in solitary ease.

My parents had been rid of the illness they shared for some years now, but it was not forgotten. My mother still treated my father vindictively. A good-hearted woman to everyone else, her husband was the only person in the world she could show no feeling for. Maybe she hated him because he was the only person in the world who had known her in the embarrassment of desire. Maybe she was vindictive because she had no faith in her power to hurt. Whatever the cause, the breach between them was an injury that had always intimidated their children.

_14._

A HOUSE IS LIKE A MOLD that forms the character and nature of the amorphous child that is born and grows up inside it, giving that nature a shape that does not always fit into the shapes of other houses, or move comfortably about in a larger world when the character grows and becomes a man. When he walks the world's streets, his rough edges rub against others or press back into himself hurtfully if he tries to fit his shape into a pattern for which he is not intended. His may be a shape that has weak parts or a vulnerable center that get battered and have to be reshaped, recreated. Or it may be a form that never finds its fit, and is destroyed by living.

Life was a painful experience to me after I left school and tried to make my living with men and women I never felt at home with. And it continued so for many years, an admitted agony that I endured, either because I hadn't the courage to end it, or because I had the innocence to believe that eventually I would find a place among other lives that would prove my potential and enable me to count among them and feel some of that great peace that I had sensed was man's right when, as a child, I had first looked upon infinity.

One night in October, a year or two after my visit home, I had a telephone call from Treva. She was in Freedom visiting our parents, but she planned to take the morning train for Kansas City where she would catch a plane to Houston. Could I meet her in Kansas City? She would be at the Muehlbach. She would be able to spend the afternoon with me. The next day was a Sunday. I was free to go.

Treva was in her early forties now. She had begun to age gracefully, with a beauty about her that had fully ripened. I noticed that she was dressed very simply, as if to make an effort for *chic* were somehow unbecoming. She wore no jewelry except for a large emerald ring that she had inherited when Mrs. Murray died. And she was exquisitely groomed. It was raining outside and so we stayed in her room and talked. "It's very depressing to go home now," she said. She seemed remorseful. "Mother and Dad are both so old, and they still seem to hate each other. It would seem that in their old age they might try to get along and make the best of things. Dad would. But Mother can't."

I suggested that we take a taxi and go out to the art museum where there was an exhibition of Vuillard, but Treva didn't want to leave the hotel.

"Please, Joey. I want to talk. I've got to talk with someone, I feel, or I'll scream." She lighted a cigarette and paced the floor of the small room. I was daunted by the anxiety she appeared to be feeling. I couldn't imagine the cause. At last she spoke out: "I must tell you something very personal, Joey." I waited, having no idea what she was going to say next and then it came. "Joey, I've never known real love."

With this announcement, the rain suddenly seemed very dismal, and the gray, drizzling atmosphere outside our window made all of life seem cheerless and cold. "I mean it, Joey. I've never been able really to . . . to give myself. I . . . I just can't do it. It's as if something had frozen inside me that couldn't thaw. I've never known love." She began to cry. I was not prepared for this revelation. Ever since the day of my first awareness of sexual relations, I had secretly supposed that my sister Treva might have enjoyed gratifying romances with two or three young men before she got married, and it would not have shocked me at this time to hear that she was having a discreet affair outside her home. "No, Joey. Jule was right about me. I was just a tease. I was terrified of any man who really expected anything serious of me."

"Like that one boyfriend?" I asked, unable then to re-call the name *Frank Bradshaw.*

"Do you want to know something, Joey? I still hear from him once in a while. He was in Houston last year and called me. Clint wasn't home. Frank wanted me to meet him at his hotel, and I wanted to so terribly, but I couldn't."

"Why not?" I asked.

"Well, Joey." She sounded shocked. "After all, I'm a married woman with grown children. How would I feel if Clint ever found out? I couldn't live with the feeling I was hiding something from him."

"Many women do," I said, "and men, too, of course."

Treva faced herself more honestly then. "I was afraid to go. I was always afraid of myself with Frank. There was something so strong about him that demanded love as his right. And he demanded something serious of me in return. I don't know what to call it. Honesty, maybe. Honesty to myself. He always made me feel very humble. Isn't that sratnge? Because I was very much in love with him. Love makes us humble, Joey, if we're ever brave enough to experience it. I was so arrogant when I first met Frank. And vain. Love was such a simple, everyday kind of thing, I couldn't recognize it."

"Aren't you and Clint happy?"

"I don't feel I've been a very good wife. I don't think I've made him very happy. I've tried but it's not the same when you have to try. I'm a good hostess and run the house well, and his friends find me attractive, but we live as separate people trying not to get too much in each other's way."

This confession saddened me. Treva had been the one person in my family I had always looked to as a proof that happiness could be attained somehow within the framework of our common heritage. Her story left me feeling we were a family doomed to failure in the process of living.

"I could have found love with Frank Bradshaw if I'd been brave enough," she spoke again after a long silence. "But now it's too late. I hate to think I'll die, Joey, without ever knowing what real fulfillment is. I'm afraid I'll die, unused."

That evening we had dinner in the dining room in the hotel, and then I took her in a taxi to the airport. It was the last time I ever saw her. She died of cancer the following spring.

Deaths come in rapid succession when one approaches one's middle years. Aunt Patsy survived World War II, and then died of an internal hemorrhage at the age of seventy-six. I was giving final exams and was too busy to attend the funeral, but I saw Uncle Merlin a few weeks later. He was a broken man, sitting in a house full of marauding cats and filthy odors that he was unaware of. He did not remember one evil or disgusting thing Patsy had ever done. He remembered only the pretty girl he had married, before age and avarice had ever touched her. "She was such a sweet girl, Joey," he sobbed. "I can't find anything to live for now she's gone." And his death followed hers in the few months that it takes for the body to give up its functions after the heart is dead.

My father died in the mid-Forties. He and Mother had been living together as invalids for several years, in a little cottage they bought after getting rid of the big house they had raised their family in. My sister Grace and I provided a practical nurse and a housekeeper for them. Mother had suffered a stroke a few years before, and was brought back from the hospital unable to walk, and with the mentality of a mischievous little girl. Now, her reason gone, she was irrationally jealous of every woman who applied for the job of housekeeper. Finally, in her mindlessness, she could admit that she loved my father. She would accuse each woman of meaning to seduce him, would insult her, order her to leave the house. Then one day, Grace found a woman named Ethel, who was in her late fifties, a strong enough woman to shame Mother out of her childish suspicions. She surrendered to Ethel's gentle command, and Ethel stayed and nursed both my parents like sick children.

I could not attend my father's funeral. I was in a hospital in Kansas City at the time, having suffered a breakdown in the middle of the second semester, in the early spring. I let others attribute my illness, euphemistically, to overwork; but I myself knew it to be the final wreckage of my childhood, whose ideals and ambitions and strivings could no longer hope for realization. I was thirty-six at the time. And age stood before me like a cavern. I hated my life. I could not live with the feeling of failure I inflicted upon myself. I was grieved that I could not honor my father at his funeral. I felt remiss that we had never shared any closeness. We had lived like two tourists from the same land, who fail to meet in a foreign country.

At the time of my father's death, I was in a closely supervised ward of the hospital where male patients were not allowed to keep their razor blades nor any sharp instruments, and where the windows were secured as in a prison. But in a prison, the inmates have the benefit of each other's company and conversation. In the hospital, each inmate was locked inside himself and conversation among us, any kind of companionship, could not exist. We were watched constantly by the nurses and attendants. We were forbidden to enter the room of another patient. I was not irrational, as most of the patients were, but suffering acute depression. Suicide was not an intention, and the doctors' and nurses' treatment of me as a possible suicide was a constant discouragement, giving me the feeling that I was expected to kill myself or at least to make an attempt. Their constant vigilance could not but make me feel that the wish for us all to destroy ourselves was the father to their thought that we might. For, accompanying the shock and possible bereavement we feel upon hearing of a friend's suicide, isn't there also a feeling of fulfillment somewhere very deep inside of us, a fulfillment of the inherent longing we all feel for death? In this we are like homesick voyagers who, even while they enjoy "seeing the sights" of a foreign land, contain a plaintive longing for their home. And how often do we truly share another person's happiness and successes? Don't we force ourselves to congratulate the friend? Doesn't his success estrange us from him?

Doesn't it make us bitter and disappointed in our own lives?

I had become so bitter and disappointed in my own life that I had made a halfhearted, unsuccessful attempt to destroy it. That is why I was incarcerated in the hospital. I had felt a genuine wish to die when, after a long depression that sometimes weighed so heavily upon me I could not meet my classes, I one night grabbed a handful of sleeping pills and gulped them down with whiskey. It was a depression that grew out of my failure to perform some creative work that would single me out (how intensely the individual can loathe his simple, human kinship to all men and want to rise above it) and distinguish me as one who was truly gifted and thus superior. Ambition had drawn me away from men and I had come to live more and more inside my own world of thoughts and fancies. But, granted my wish to die, I made the attempt upon my life, also, out of some infantile craving to be attended to, to feel someone's concern over me, even though the only concern that I experienced was the very professional sort that I bought, as it were, from my doctor and the nurses who attended me. Sometimes one is driven to desperate actions to discover whether one is loved. I didn't discover love by my actions, but I did discover that the head of my department, at the college where I taught, was most considerate of me and saw to it that my salary continued while I was in the hospital, and several times visited me, reassuring me that my work had been much more than satisfactory (I had come to feel myself a failure in every part of my life) and that he would try to get me a raise in salary the following year. His concern heartened me.

There was a most interesting young woman in the "closed ward" of the hospital when I entered. A patient, too. Her Christian name was Marsha. I had heard her perform at a piano recital once on a weekend trip to St. Louis. All of the city of St. Louis knew of her great talent; few knew of her emotional instability. She was unusually gifted. And she was also beautiful, with black hair and a fair white skin, and dark eyes that held the tragedy of her suffering, and gave her beauty its sensitive nobility. She was in her early twenties. I was to discover later that she was a schizophrenic who suffered attacks of severe paranoia, and that the hospital's prognosis for her case was not encouraging. I am glad I did not know all that at the time I was a patient with her.

One night, a young Swedish steelworker was brought into the ward in a straitjacket, which the male attendants immediately removed from him once the thick, heavy door was safely closed behind them, locking automatically. The young Swede was tall and powerful, on his handsome face an expression of ferocity and hate. He looked about him once he was freed of the jacket, and paced the floor of the lounge where we were permitted to play cards or put together picture puzzles, like a great panther just brought into captivity. And he was silent as a panther, his physical movement as coordinated and full of suspense and animal rhythm. He stared at Marsha. Desire roused him fast. Then he seized her, like a panther its prey, and sped with her to his room, holding her with one powerful arm, the other swinging free as the attendants who, not having perceived his intention at once, were felled like saplings by his strokes.

Of course there were no locks inside the doors of the patients' cells or rooms, but each room was small, a cubicle, and the young Swede's room was just the length of his single bed which he quickly pulled out from one side of the room to barricade the door, which could not be opened now. The attendants rushed out of the ward to report to their superiors. The entire hospital was in a state of alarm. Nurses, doctors, attendants ran through the corridors like the Furies, all on futile errands of prevention. The young Swede had fooled them. They had no way to keep him from ravishing the girl he had carried off to his room.

The door to each room, of course, had a tiny window to enable the nurses to spy inside at any time to see if a patient was endangering himself. Some of their concern now was natural and humane. They did not know if Marsha's life was safe. Thus, a white-capped nurse remained at the door to the room to keep watch through the tiny window. The other patients were not allowed to come near the window; we could only guess at what was happening to Marsha by watching the features on the nurse's face. For a long time they were immobile. And then a maidenly blush filled her fleshy cheeks and, in modesty, she turned her head. It was not an act of violence the young Swede was performing. He and Marsha were free now to gratify their sweet desire for each other (for Marsha confessed later to her doctor that she had responded encouragingly to the young man's first look of longing before he seized her) for almost two hours before the attendants and the janitors on the staff were able to get a ladder dispatched from the city fire department, high enough to take them to the window of the young Swede's cell and crash its reinforced glass with picks and axes, by which time the two young people had sated their desire.

Thereafter, the beds were chained to the walls of the patients' rooms so that they could never again be used to bar entrance. And the hospital staff were mortified for days at not having foreseen the possibility of such an occurrence. The Swede and Marsha had to endure the most vigilant supervision to prevent their ever again so fracturing the institution's discipline. They were, like criminals, under constant observation for the rest of their stay.

Once in a while, I would see the exchange of wistful glances between them, while we patients sat dumbly in the lounge — it was some years prior to the ubiquity of television — some of us trying to take interest in card games or the picture puzzles, listening to inane radio programs, trying not to show awareness of the cries of the totally maddened in their rooms; the obscene cursings of a former clergyman who would defecate in his bed and fling his dung at the walls; the hopeless moanings of a woman (a former schoolteacher) who had lost her reason during menopause.

And once, when those of us who were able and were granted permission to have our noon meal in the hospital's commissary were passing together out of the ward, I caught a glimpse of the Swede taking hold of Marsha's hand as we all walked together down the corridor, and she looking high up into his pale blue eyes and smiling like the sudden blossom of a flower. The nurses saw it happen, too. Their expressions were stern and forbidding. They exchanged glances among themselves, as if to ask, Should we permit this kind of thing to happen? Are these two patients breaking a rule? But apparently conscience prompted them, they could not rightfully prevent two people from holding hands, so a look of disapproval unspoken, was their only comment on the gesture.

I saw in the institutional treatment of Marsha and the young Swede a similarity to the treatment of the young students in the girls' school I taught in, a school located close to a military academy where many unruly boys were sent, the parents of students in both schools hoping that others could make up for their own failure in disciplining their children. The members of the administration of the girls' school were terrified that a girl might become pregnant while enrolled there. When this happened, it brought the parents' wrath upon them and threatened the school's enrollment, should it become reputed as a school lax in governing its students. Thus, concern over the students' virginity became a paramount issue, superseding even the concern over their education.

At school dances, two or three buses would arrive from the military academy, full of handsomely uniformed cadets who would file into the ballroom to dance with the waiting, expectant girls. Male members of the faculty were assigned patrol of all corridors and the surrounding grounds to prevent any from escaping the party to make their private Eden in the bushes or a hidden alcove. After the party ended, the cadets were herded back into the waiting buses like young steers, their officers checking their names off a roster as each boy returned to their custody, then the buses could roll smoothly out of town back to the academy, and members of both faculties could relax at last, now that their vigilance over virginity was ended. No young couple had managed to escape their patrol and find a few moments of private ecstasy together. Of course, it sometimes happened that a couple did elude the close surveillance and sported themselves to the almost frantic disapproval of their educational guardians. When such a happening occurred, the members of the administrations of the schools were mortified and disapproving, much like the members of the hospital staff.

I was held in the closed ward of the hospital only the usual two weeks. When I was released into the open ward, Marsha was also. And two weeks later, the young Swede. Then Marsha was free to play the piano. She and "Swede" were permitted to be "friendly" but were not allowed off the grounds together. Here, we had the freedom of the grounds and were allowed occasional trips into town to see a film or shop or have dinner. We saw our doctors every day. I once asked my doctor if, sexual and love relations being a troubling complexity for just about every patient in the hospital, he didn't think that patients, those who felt a mutual attraction, should not be permitted to fulfill their physical desires for one another. He thought long before asking me in return, "What if one of the young women became pregnant?" I was bold enough to suggest that the nurses educate them, if necessary, in methods of prevention. The doctor shook his head. "Public opinion would be against it. We'd find ourselves in trouble immediately with families and patrons."

"But isn't it the duty of medical science to function on a higher plane of thought than public opinion?" He didn't answer. I went on to say, "Inasmuch as love and sex are such frightening experiences for most patients, wouldn't it be helpful if they were free to have these experiences here where their immediate reactions of fear, guilt, shame, could be dealt with? Can you ever give the utmost in help and treatment to a patient in a constantly protected environment?" He admitted that *perhaps* some day in the future, hospitals would come to permit this freedom.

One day, sitting in my room, reading, I heard Marsha in the lounge playing a piece I thought I recognized, a Schubert sonata, but for some reason, now the music held me and I felt the depth of its beauty as I never had been able to before. It was as though a spell had been cast over me. I felt an inner peace and harmony that seemed to transcend the boundaries of all the world and reach out into universal space and eternity. What had created such beauty? Spirit. Spirit alone, with physical labor its servant. I put down my book and listened not with just my ears, but with my entire being. I knew then that I had never listened to music before but had only heard it. Listening was a total involvement. I was beginning to recover by this time, that I could so fully give myself to experience, without holding any part of me back, without making reservations. It was an experience I can only call *sublime.* Marsha's playing of the music was of course brilliant. If there had been the tiniest flaw in her performance, the spell could have broken. But it was not. I could take the perfection for granted. It was the beauty of eternity I was feeling again, for the first time since I was a boy.

I left the hospital after three months and continued treatment with a doctor in Kansas City for several more years, commuting there by train. These were troubled years but ones in which I felt rewarded from time to time by an awareness of personal growth that gave me increasing strength. But the breakdown had left me with a few restrictive fears that only time, if anything, could conquer. One of these was a traumatic fear of driving an automobile. When I first tried it, I panicked behind the wheel. So, for several years, I did not attempt to make this unconscious competition with the long-deceased Jule. But slowly I began to derive more fulfillment from my teaching, even to enjoy it. I learned to live peacefully with my feeling of failure. Eventually I was able to drive again without fear. But at times, I still dreaded my aloneness like a corridor that has no end.

15.

O NE SATURDAY when I was in Kansas City, browsing
in a bookstore after seeing my doctor, I saw Betsy.
We stared at each other, and then smiled before we spoke,
as if amused that our seeing one another again should have
happened so precariously. There in the bookstore, we embraced, and I recognized the long forgotten aroma of her
person that had once been so close to me. "Joey-pie!" she
breathed into my ear, her cheek clamped next to mine; and
it was like discovering treasure to find that we still cared
for each other so deeply.

I didn't want to let her go. "Have lunch with me," I
begged.

"All right, I'll just do that. I'll call home and tell the
housekeeper she and the kids can just go screw themselves,
that I'm having lunch downtown with one of my dearest
friends."

She was radiant and healthy. But there was a domestic-
ity about her that surprised me. I took us to the Muehlbach,
where I had not been since my last meeting with Treva.

"This calls for a drink, Betsy. Shall I order a bottle of champagne?"

"Oh, not for me, Joey. I never touch it any more."

"Really?" I asked, puzzled, remembering how as a student she had loved to drink.

"Well . . . It's a long story, Joey." I waited. "I'm an A.A." I must have looked blank. "Alcoholics Anonymous."

"Oh," I said, remembering having heard something of the organization, but not knowing precisely what it was. Then she began her story, which lasted through my one daiquiri and a three-course luncheon.

"It takes more than talent, Joey," she ended over coffee. "It takes guts I don't have to get anywhere on Broadway. I had one tiny part in a play that flopped, and then came a series of getting beaten up by lovers, and getting dragged off to Bellevue to get over the D.T.'s. God, I was miserable. I can't tell you what the misery was. And it all seems so needless now. Like a spasm life put me through, until I came to my senses."

"You had a beautiful talent," I said gravely.

She smiled. "Thank you, Joey. I like to think I did, of course. And once in a while, I have a few regrets. Particularly, when Joe and I . . . Isn't that funny, that I married a man named Joe? . . . when Joe and I go to the theater and I see some trollop on stage not doing half of what I feel I could do with the part. But I have something else I wouldn't trade her, not for anything in the world."

"What's that?" I asked.

"Serenity," she said, in a small, sure voice that was full of humility. She was speaking very personally to me now, I felt, and very truthfully. "I found out something, Joey. I believe in God. I guess I've always believed in Him, even during the wildest, craziest times in my life. But I never really *knew* that I believed in Him, or that He was waiting for me to come to Him, like a patient father, and say . . . 'I'm sorry. I've made a mess of things. I've never understood You all these years, and never realized what life really was. I know now that You don't punish people. I know You sit back in Your throne very troubled to see that people punish themselves.' That's all I was doing before I found this out, Joey. Punishing myself."

"Your husband and children?"

"Oh, only one of the kids is mine. The baby. A year old now. The other two are Joe's by his first marriage. Joe is an A.A., too. That's where I met him. He's a building contractor and makes a very good living for us, even though he has to pay his first wife a scandalous alimony. But maybe she deserves it. I know he must have put her through some pretty rough times in his drinking days. He admits it. He hasn't taken a drink now in eight years. It's been three for me. We go to church every Sunday. Would you believe it? And we still go to our group meetings every Thursday night. We couldn't live without those weekly meetings. Each one gives us a new supply of peace that lasts us until the next week. It's like oxygen. You wouldn't believe it, what simple lives we lead. We stay home at night and read, or maybe take in a movie. I wake up each morning, so happy to face the day. And I've learned to cook, as a kind of hobby, and once in a while we have dinner guests. Usually other A.A.'s, because it makes Joe mad to have to buy liquor now to serve friends. He says it's the silliest extravagance he ever heard of." She giggled at the bit of irony. "We serve it, though, when company wants it. Neither of us has any desire at all to drink."

"Don't you think you could have found this . . . this serenity," I asked, "if you'd gone on with your career?"

She thought for several moments. "You mean . . . maybe I'm not facing the world? Could I be happy and use my talent, too?"

"It's just that I hate to see such a fine talent go to waste."

"Don't, Joey," she pleaded, tears suddenly coming to her eyes. "I don't like to think I'm going to waste."

"Maybe you're not. I don't know." I was sorry to have asked my question.

She said soberly, "I really don't know, Joey, if I could go back to the theater, maybe even becoming a star, and keep my sanity. I just don't know. But my life is *not* wasted. I'm a good mother, and I do lots of things to help others. Most acting is just an indulgence, and actors are the most selfish people in the world."

And yet the book she had bought in the bookshop was a

play. When I pointed this out, she said, "Oh yes. It's *A Streetcar Named Desire*. Have you seen it, Joey?"

I said that I hadn't — in fact, I hadn't taken much interest in the theater since I'd left college. But I had heard of it.

"Oh, it *is* the most divine play. Joe and I saw it when he took me to New York a few weeks ago on a business trip. I admit, I left the theater feeling some very deep regrets. Wouldn't I have made a wonderful Blanche? Tennessee Williams is really a genius. It's the most exciting American play I ever saw."

She fell silent. After a moment, she said, "You know something, Joey? We never learn what life is all about until we fail." I asked her to explain. "Well, it's as though I had wanted all the time to become an actress just to have my own way about something, and I really don't know what the something was. But I was ambitious in the wrong way. It's almost as though I wanted to be a brilliant success in the theater in order to have vengeance on someone . . . I don't know who. Maybe the world. So I missed. I know I had talent. But I was using it the wrong way. It was *I* who messed up my chances. I alone. I had to give up my conception of what my life was going to be, do you see? My *will* had to be overcome. I had to learn that there's a stronger will that works behind the entire universe that sometimes stops us in our headstrong way and says No. And then you have to surrender to a real life, Joey. The life that's really yours. And make the very best you can out of the life that you have to lead. Understand what I mean? Or am I being too metaphysical, or something?"

"I think I understand something of what you mean, Betsy. I think I do."

After lunch, we parted. All the rest of the day, I thought of Betsy, feeling somehow I had witnessed one of Christ's miracles. And yet, though she had asked me to come out to visit her and her husband, I knew it was unlikely that I would. I could not help feeling apart from them, for they had already become a fixed part of what outsiders call with some derision, some envy, the *normal* world, the world of people who come home at night to ordinary meals, enjoy ordinary companionship, and suffer ordinary appetites and desires, a world I often curse, like Lucifer the heaven from which he had been expelled, knowing that I am *not* Lucifer and that it is a false heaven I long at times to return to, wishing to God I could still find comfort in its solidarity and mirage of warmth, feeling at times I would be willing to hate Negroes, or condemn Jews, and pretend to worship God while I worshipped Mammon, if I could feel once again the assurance of belonging to the great mass of people who live their lives without conscience or reflection, and subscribe to mass opinion as my father subscribed to *Time* magazine, never challenging its precepts.

But once the mold is cast, the form cannot be changed. The shape of me could no longer fit into other people's houses. I cannot claim that Betsy and her husband are hypocrites because they are happy. But sometimes, in spells of bitterness and isolation, happiness in itself has seemed an hypocrisy. And if I hated their happiness, it was because I felt a stranger to it, and a stranger to their welcome. It was a happiness that made me feel more alone.

16.

MY MOTHER LIVED five more years after my father died. She lived alone in the house with only Ethel to care for her. Whenever I was able to visit her, she was delighted as a child. Memories could still hurt her, but briefly. They would dissolve as suddenly as a child's ill temper, and then she would smile again. Treva's death, Patsy's death, and my father's, still brought momentary tears to her eyes, and if we did not quickly divert her by reminding her of some more pleasant memory, she would go into a tantrum of desperate sobbing over all the wounds that life had ever inflicted upon her. We kept the snapshot of Jule at the wheel of the old Buick, taken that summer long ago in Colorado, always on the table beside her. It always sweetened her. "My son is a splendid driver," she would brag. Sometimes she would mistake me for Jule.

"I'm not Jule, Mother. I'm Joey. Remember?"

"Oh yes, Joey."

And was it my own feeling of inadequacy that made me

imagine it, or was there actually a sound of disparagement in her voice?

Sometimes she would make inscrutable references to the past, totally out of context with anything that had happened in the recent present. Sometimes these references would be to childhood friends or events that Grace and Ethel and I had no knowledge of. One day sitting beside the window, she said in a voice that came like an echo sounding out of the past: "I wonder whose those footsteps could have been."

My sister Grace is a professor of American Literature at a Midwestern university. She got her doctorate at Columbia, writing her thesis on the novels of Willa Cather. We used to meet chiefly when our visits home to see Mother would coincide. Now we see each other once or twice a year. We are good friends. But we never talk much about the past. I don't know if she is happy. I have never felt it suitable to ask her. She keeps very busy, though, with lectures at ladies' clubs, and working on committees of one kind or another, as if she didn't want to face much of her life alone.

She tries to persuade me to write more poetry, feeling very proud of me for the little that I have written and published. But I find no strong motive for doing so. Once I had a thin volume of my poems published, and it received some very good reviews, but some very bad ones, too. Of the bad reviews, those by men were written in a mood of swashbuckling destruction; those by women, in a schoolteacher's harsh manner of correction, totally derogatory. The bad reviews were the only ones I remembered. Yet the volume was a contender for a national award, and all my childish hopes and ambitions to win a prize, to establish myself in some luminous stance for the world to see, were tempted and then unfulfilled. Thereafter, I never could write just for the pleasure and fulfillment of writing, could never resist the frustrating urge to compete, which gave an artifice to my writing, deprived it of truth, and filled it with pretension. Finally, some angered spirit inside me refused to work in a world that forces one to compete, convinced me that competition brings out the worst in us instead of the best, creates monsters, and killers of the human spirit. Had I been a better poet, I might have resisted the ugly urge.

But it often troubles me sorely, and in a way confounds me before You, that I am so unstable and so weak, so frail, in resisting my passions.

The quotation is from Thomas à Kempis. Grace joined the Catholic Church about the time she turned forty, and she found *The Imitation of Christ* a consoling book for whatever losses or misgivings she felt in her life, things she and I seldom mentioned. She persuaded me to read the book, perhaps in an effort to convert me. But it is characteristic of our friendship that she has never spoken of it to me directly.

I had never forgotten the occasion of my paternal grandmother's funeral and my father's presence there with me, a young child, sitting beside him. He was very solemn, but he did not cry until he saw them lower the coffin into its grave, and then his whole body collapsed in a spasm of hopeless sobbing, as if all his boyhood's love and need for her had been recalled. I was daunted to see my father reduced to such a childish state. But Death makes children of us all.

I felt like a child myself when I walked into the funeral parlor in my home town and saw my mother lying in her casket, surrounded by heaps of flowers whose sweet spring smell seemed such an anachronism in the setting. She had made her last journey and I wondered if she had been afraid. After my father's death, and my release from the hospital, I had visited her twice a year, never staying long, realizing there was nothing I could do to help her and knowing that she was childishly contented. And I had stopped thinking of her much. The pieces of my life were slowly coming together again now and I had to make them whole. I satisfied myself that if I wrote her a card or letter once a week, I was fulfilling the only duty I could assume to her. When Grace called long distance to tell me Mother had died, I was not aware of any very strong feeling; and on the train home, I only felt a sadness during the trip, but a kind of relief, too, for her life had been only a morbid vegetation since her stroke.

I had not expected such an eruption of feeling as had

happened to my father, but it came. The hurt and grief sprung up from some forgotten well inside me, and gushed out of my eyes like sudden rain. For a few moments, I stood there, a child in the woods. And then I became a man again, humbled and a little embarrassed to realize what an infantile love I still bore her. It was this very love that had made me miserable for so many years, and made me crave some unattainable prominence that would finally raise me above Jule in her esteem. It was a love, after Jule's death, that bound us like a silent pact, and kept me from ever loving another so deeply. It was a love that had made me hate her, at times, for it was selfish. But I couldn't hate her now. Obviously, she had felt a great need for my devotion. I could only be generous now. Somehow, she had needed my love for survival. And so, I loved her again. Death makes us all innocent, and weaves all our private hurts and griefs and wrongs into the fabric of time, and makes them part of eternity.

Mother used to tell a story about Uncle Julian, after his parents had moved from "Garden" to Oklahoma and left him and my father to run the store, and Uncle Julian had begun to drink so heavily that he could no longer do his share of the work and my father had to run the store alone. Uncle Julian would still try to come home at night to the house his parents had left behind, the house he had grown up in as a boy, that was still the only home he knew. When he was so helplessly drunk that the hotel he lived in would force him to leave, he would lie on the doorstep of the big old Victorian house that had had a *For Sale* sign posted in the front yard ever since his parents had moved. He would lie there, unconscious, sleeping off the effects of the drink he had consumed, a spectacle for schoolchildren to titter at in the morning, until the sun's heat would finally waken him and he would have to face again his homelessness. This was a story that had moved me even as a child, that Mother had always told with great pity for Uncle Julian. I applied it to myself when I looked upon my mother in her coffin. Something final happened to the past. I could never go home again, not even in fantasy, without making the same pathetic mistake of Uncle Julian. The womb of the past could no longer comfort me. I had to live my life in the confounding present.

When I recovered from the first shock of Mother's stillness, I approached closely and looked down upon her still-human face with its familiar wrinkles, and the little mole at the temple. I thought I should like to kiss her once to say goodbye. But I had never before touched a corpse prepared for burial. The softness of her once-warm cheek had turned to stone. In death, she rebuked me. I could no longer treat her with the love we give the living.

Epilogue

THERE WERE OTHER SUMMER TRIPS during my childhood, after the summer in Colorado Springs. A couple of years after that (when Jule was gone) we went to Long Beach, California, and lived the summer on the beach and at the Pike, a carnival that lasted day and night, where I had my first ride on a roller coaster and where I saw women become hysterical and scream and faint at a movie of *Blood and Sand* with Valentino. It was in Long Beach, too, where we first ate Chinese food, very suspiciously, having heard from friends among other townspeople who were summering there that the Chinese made their chop suey out of cat meat.

One summer Mother took Grace and me to visit an old friend of hers, who lived in a big Southern mansion in Greensboro, North Carolina. And there were two summers spent with Treva and Clint in Houston, none of us having any idea that Treva wasn't most happily married, probably because she and Clint impressed us with their affluence, which is so easily mistaken for happiness.

Also, we visited Niagara Falls and Washington, D.C., just as tourists.

Each trip we made, Mother still planned for with the same neurotic anxiety, but enjoyed herself with abandon once we had started. But upon each return home, she would feel a deep sadness that Jule had not been with us, and she remembered the trip to Colorado until she died as the richest enjoyment she had ever had. The trip to Colorado, for the rest of her life, was her favorite memory. And I suppose that for me, at the age of six, it was the beginning of memory, and I didn't realize when I started writing of it that it would bring me so far in my recollections.

But for me the trip to California was the most memorable because it gave me my first sight of the sea, more awesome even than the vast prairies in western Kansas. It was a daily wonder for me to gaze upon, for here was infinity spread out before me, my child's mind barely able to contain it. And here was something eternal, too, that I could realize, even then, human efforts and affairs would never change. At first, I was afraid of it. It was too big, too impersonal for me to try to swim in; and there were frightening stories told about the sea's dangerous undercurrents and riptides that could seize one like a whirlpool and pull him away from the land forever. Death did not matter to the sea, nor did any personal joy or triumph. Slowly, cautiously, I trusted myself to swim in it, always heeding Mother's warning not to get too far from the shore. I came to like the bracing cold water and the splashing waves that sometimes engulfed me and hurled me to the sandy floor, although Mother was always terrified I might drown.

The day before we were to leave Long Beach for home, I stole down to the beach at sunset. I sat alone until I forgot time, and gazed at the sea as if hoping to fill my eyes with a vision I'd never forget of a world so vast that human affairs would always seem small by comparison and lose their power to hurt. And once in a while, in life or in art, I still experience this same sublimity.